The Mira...
MUSIC
THERAPY

Rajendar Menen

PUSTAK MAHAL®
Delhi•Bangalore•Mumbai•Patna•Hyderabad•London

Publishers
Pustak Mahal®, Delhi

J-3/16 , Daryaganj, New Delhi-110002
☎ 23276539, 23272783, 23272784 • *Fax:* 011-23260518
E-mail: info@pustakmahal.com • *Website:* www.pustakmahal.con

London Office
51, Severn Crescents, Slough, Berkshire, SL 38 UU, England
E-mail: pustakmahaluk@pustakmahal.com

Sales Centre
10-B, Netaji Subhash Marg, Daryaganj, New Delhi-110002
☎ 23268292, 23268293, 23279900 • *Fax:* 011-23280567
E-mail: rapidexdelhi@indiatimes.com

Branch Offices
Bangalore: ☎ 22234025
E-mail: pmblr@sancharnet.in • pustak@sancharnet.in
Mumbai: ☎ 22010941
E-mail: rapidex@bom5.vsnl.net.in
Patna: ☎ 3294193 • *Telefax:* 0612-2302719
E-mail: rapidexptn@rediffmail.com
Hyderabad: *Telefax:* 040-24737290
E-mail: pustakmahalhyd@yahoo.co.in

© **Pustak Mahal, Delhi**

ISBN 978-81-223-0806-8

Edition : 2008

Printed at : Aggarwal Printing Press, Delhi

DEDICATION

This book is dedicated to Anna and the music of rain-drenched summers in County Kerry.

Acknowledgement

I am grateful to all the literature available on the subject. I have learnt a lot and it has also helped me put together a book I hope you will like and benefit from.

Contents

Preface

Ever since I can remember, I have been fascinated by music. I use the word 'fascinated' with some deliberation and care because I am far from the regular music buff you see strolling into or out of a music shop with a tune on his or her lips. I am tone deaf, can't sing to stop the shower, don't see films of any kind especially those ransacked by cheap, lilting music and can live for days on a diet of silence broken probably by the exaggerated noise of a falling twig against the hush of soundlessness.

But give me the grand opera, music festivals in any city in the world, jazz in Temple Bar or New Orleans, the deep-throated resonance of Osho and the spiritualists in India, Tibet, Japan or any part of the world, the tinker of the instrumentalists, or even the grand festivity of pop and rock, and you have my life on a platter.

It doesn't matter if you can't sing. It doesn't matter if you can't hear. But if you can grasp the magic that music brings to all life, you are there. Where it matters.

Music makes you happy. Simply put.

But it also takes you to a platform far removed from the mundane theatre of our lives. From there we conduct the opera of our choice. From there we laugh, we cry, we reminisce, we choose our emotion and escape to an extraordinary passion handpicked from our dreams. From there we drop all mortal sin and the weariness of ordinary life. From there we stake claims to immortality. From there we harness the sunset. Our hopes soar, and we begin to believe in life once more... the roses are in bloom and the dew glistens on the green... Yes, music is all this and much, much more.

Writing this book has been exciting. I have learnt a lot and met and spoken to scores of people whose lives have changed after music discovered it. The scope of the book is endless and so I had to pick and choose areas for the larger interest of the reader. We have deliberately kept out cults and religious organisations though their music is undoubtedly exhilarating and therapeutic. We simply wanted to give music therapy the neutral stance it deserves.

There are millions and zillions of musical scores available. In every genre. Take your pick. And rejoice in the fact that if you are elevated by the music of your choice from the weariness of earthly existence, even if it is only for a fleeting moment, what could be a better definition of heaven?

Enjoy!

—Rajendar Menen

Part I
ANCIENT HEALING
REDISCOVERED

1. The Specialised Use of Music

Music is a universal language. It influences all levels of human existence. It is a medium for communication, which can be both a pleasant and healing experience. Modern science and medicine are now rediscovering the healing powers of music. And music therapy – the specialised use of music in treating persons with special needs in mental and physical health, rehabilitation and special education – is gaining ground. In the West it is now an accepted form of treatment even within orthodox medical practice.

Music is an age-old part of Ayurveda, the holistic Indian science that promotes a happy and healthy lifestyle. From time immemorial, music has been a part of Indian culture. In the Vedas too, music has an important place. The Samveda is full of music. Doshas like Vata, Pitta and Kapha can be controlled effectively through music therapy. Great composers of Indian classical music have attempted music therapy down the years. Legend has it that classical music maestro Thyagaraja brought a dead person back to life with a composition of his.

It is believed that music stimulates the pituitary gland, whose secretions affect the nervous system and the flow of blood. To be healed by music, it is necessary to vibrate the cells of the body, for it is through these vibrations that the diseased person's consciousness can be changed effectively to promote health. The right kind of music helps one relax and refresh. Even during the course of working, light music improves efficiency.

Listening to music helps control negative aspects of our personality like worry, bias and anger. In addition, it can help cure headache, abdominal pain and tension. Music therapy is one of the most effective ways of controlling emotions, blood pressure and restoring the functioning of the liver.

Music therapy is an efficacious and valid treatment for persons who have psychosocial, affective, cognitive and communicative needs. Research results and clinical experiences attest to the viability of music therapy even in those who are resistive to other treatment approaches. Music is a form of sensory stimulation that provokes responses due to the familiarity, predictability and feelings of security associated with it.

Music therapists use music activities, both instrumental and vocal, which are designed to facilitate changes that are non-musical in nature. Music therapy programmes are based on individual assessment, treatment planning, and ongoing programme evaluation. Frequently functioning as members of an interdisciplinary team, music therapists implement programmes with groups or individuals that display a vast continuum of needs, from reduction of anxiety to deeper self-understanding.

Music therapists work with the interdisciplinary team to assess emotional well-being, physical health, social functioning, communication abilities, and cognitive skills through musical responses. When individualised music experiences are designed by the music therapist to fit functional abilities and needs, responses may be immediate and readily apparent. Clients need not have a music background to benefit from music therapy.

The Raga Research Centre in Chennai, India is currently making a comprehensive study of Indian ragas and evaluating their therapeutic potential with the help of musicians, doctors and psychiatrists. It is believed that classical Indian ragas can benefit a host of conditions ranging from insomnia, high and low blood pressure to schizophrenia and epilepsy. Research is also underway to understand how it can fight ageing and pain.

Music is capable of improving happiness, peace, health and concentration. It is, however, important to know the method and duration for which music therapy is to be administered. This knowledge can be obtained through regular experiments and experience. The first step towards this is the correct diagnosis of the disease and then the selection of the precise raga that will be helpful. Procedure, discipline and a systematic method will help achieve this goal.

Music can play an effective role in helping us lead better, fruitful lives. Listening to specific kinds of music at specific times of the day has been shown to be helpful in maintaining good health.

Indian music, with its many ragas, is known to be particularly therapeutic in value. The curative power of music emanates from the resonance of certain ragas on hormonal and glandular functions, which produce secretions that keep the body balanced and infection free.

For example, *Ahir Bhairav* helps indigestion, *Asavari* helps build confidence, *Bageshri* is good for insomnia, *Basant Bahar* for gall-stones, *Bhairavi* for rheumatic arthritis, *Bhim Palas* for anxiety, *Chandrakauns* for anorexia and so on... The list is long and quite comprehensive with detailed ragas for specific disorders.

❏ ❏ ❏

2. Facilitating Communication

Music therapy is special in its use of music to encourage communication and expression by playing an instrument, singing or listening, usually through improvised music. The therapist does not teach the client to play an instrument; the instruments offered can all be played intuitively.

Within the therapeutic relationship, there is a safe setting in which difficult or repressed feelings can be expressed and contained. Where words are inadequate (or even impossible), music can often make sense. In the restricted world of a seriously ill child, music therapy focuses on what s/he can do, gives choices and control, and raises self-esteem.

A music therapist at one children's hospice talks about one session: "J suffers from Duchenne Muscular Dystrophy at quite an advanced stage, can no longer eat or drink by himself, and is totally dependent for all his care. During a recent session he played on drum and cymbal. After ten minutes J said he had had enough, adding apologetically 'My hand is weak, as is my arm, as am I.' The music, however, had been vigorous, energetic and full of exciting accelerandi. No sign of weakness there. J had been involved in an experience which transcended his bodily limitations."

At another hospice: "A small child had spent the morning distressed and crying, very tense and jerky physically. At first I held his hands or feet and sang back to him, responding to his rather chaotic sounds and movements and then introducing more order and rhythm. Leaving silences led to his increased awareness of his contact with me, and the realisation that he could initiate the music and movement.

This led to a vocal interaction, many times over, and he also played a hand-held wind chime positioned just where he could play it. He began to smile and became calm, relaxed and communicative by the end of the session."

❏ ❏ ❏

3. Rediscovering an Ancient Healing Technique

Seven years ago, Peter Fisher (name changed), a 60-year-old physician in Ohio, was driving to work when he recognised the symptoms of an impending stroke: bright flashing lights, numbness, headache. Calmly, he pulled into a petrol pump, leaned on his horn and asked the terrified attendant to call an ambulance to take him to a specific hospital. The only movement he had was his eyelids, and his only means of communication was blinking once for yes, twice for no.

A few weeks later, Peter's desperate wife placed a call to Don Campbell, a composer, music researcher, healer and author who we have also quoted in the book. He suggested that they play as much Mozart as possible in Peter's room, and a few weeks after that, he paid a personal visit. "I sat on the right side of the bed, because the right ear is the quickest way to the language centres of the brain, and began to sing and simultaneously tap each syllable into his hand," recalls Campbell. "For the next three hours, I would sing and tap for five minutes, then rest for 10 minutes."

At the end of the session, the two men were actually communicating with a codified system by which Fisher would indicate letters with eye movements.

This experience, which Campbell terms integrated auditory patterning, enabled Peter to begin to reconnect with the outside world. A few months later he was fitted with a light-emitting cap, which activates computer keys when it is directed at them. Now in a wheelchair, Peter writes journals and keeps in touch with his family and former colleagues.

Ironically, three years after participating in Peter's rehabilitation, Campbell, then a robust 43-year-old, learned that he had a potentially fatal blood clot in an artery just below his brain. He was given three options: undergo immediate surgery with no guarantee of a positive outcome; be admitted to the hospital for six weeks for hourly monitoring; or simply wait a few days and see what happens.

Campbell, who'd spent 10 years investigating the effects of sound on the body, was quite knowledgeable about therapeutic uses of music. So he decided to pass on the surgery and hospitalisation and simply hum. Fearful that a more powerful sound might bring on a stroke, he hummed quietly for three to four minutes at a time, up to seven times a day. He did this for three weeks, at the same time meditating on healing images.

Don Campbell used sound therapy to prevent a stroke.

He went back for a second brain scan, and when his doctor saw the results, he was speechless: The blood clot had shrunk from more than an inch and a half in length to an eighth of an inch, and Campbell was proclaimed out of danger.

"Sound therapy" may seem like just the latest New Age fad, but in fact it dates back thousands of years. "The use of sound and music is the most ancient healing modality," says Jonathan Goldman, founder and director of the Sound Healers Association from Colorado, and author of *Healing Sounds* (1996). "It was practised in the ancient mystery schools of Egypt, Tibet, India, Athens and Rome for tens of thousands of years. Much of this information disappeared in the West, but it's been re-emerging in the last 10 or 15 years."

Even if you didn't know that a thousand years ago the Chinese believed music could do everything from transform people's characters to restore the fertility of the soil, you do know that sound is a powerful force. Most of us, at one time or another, practise our own version of music therapy. We instinctually make — or seek out — sound to express our emotions. A mother naturally sings to soothe her baby. When we're depressed, we play or make our favourite music, either to lift us out of our gloom or to intensify it; when happy, we play joyous music to enhance the mood.

Pythagoras trained students to release negative emotions through music.

We're in good company. In *The Iliad*, Apollo, the mythical god of music and medicine, halted a plague because he was so pleased with the sacred hymns sung by Greek youths. Pythagoras, who discovered that all music could be expressed in numbers and mathematical formulae, founded a school that, among other things, trained students to release worry, fear, anger and sorrow through singing and playing musical instruments.

Music is a fundamental component of all major religions, from Christian hymns to Jewish cantorial melodies to the muezzin calling Muslims to prayer. Buddhists recite mantras and prayers and chant to win merit in this life and those to come. Millions of people around the world chant the Sanskrit mantra 'Aum' daily to purify mind and body and become one with all creation. Sufis (the esoteric branch of Islam) hold that higher states of consciousness can be attained by concentrating on the reverberations of bells and the harmonic echoes of choirs. And Judaism's mystical Kabbala teaches that chanting certain vowel sounds connects one with the energies of the Divine.

Don Campbell may be one of the leading American pioneers in his field, but the man he calls the Einstein of sound is Alfred Tomatis, MD, a Frenchman who's devoted his life to the study of the human ear and the effects of musical sound on the brain. It was Tomatis who first established that foetuses can hear sound.

Back in the 1960s, the Paris-based physician was called in to investigate a strange malaise that had overtaken a monastery of Benedictine monks in the south of France. Out of the blue, the brothers had become listless, tired and depressed. Once other medical authorities had ruled out physical causes, Tomatis began to search for changes in their diet or work conditions but discovered none.

After a lengthy discussion with the monks, however, Tomatis learned that before they took ill, the monks used to gather eight or nine times a day and chant for 10 to 20 minutes. But thanks to the reforms of Vatican II, their daily chanting had been reduced by several hours a day. It dawned on Tomatis that the physiological benefits of their chanting – slowing down their breathing, lowering their blood pressure and elevating their mood and productivity – were at the heart of the monk's lethargy.

His solution: restoring their full sonic regimen of Gregorian chants. The effects were dramatic. Within six months, the monks were back to their old vigorous and healthy selves.

According to Tomatis, all cranial nerves lead to the ear, which explains why soothing musical harmonics not only induce states of deep relaxation, but directly affect breathing, the voice, the heart rate and digestion. In fact, Tomatis' research has led him to theorise that sacred chants from various religious traditions "charge" the cortex of the brain, which sheds light on the transformative power of certain musical and vocal sounds.

Herbert Benson, MD, of the Mind/Body Medical Institute at Boston's Deaconess Medical Centre and author of *Timeless Healing, The Power and Biology of Belief* (1996), has studied the effects of chanting mantras on human physiology. He has found that by repeating a single word (such as Aum), measurable changes are produced in energy consumption, respiration rate, heartbeat, pulse and metabolic rate. An increase in alpha brain waves, associated with daydreaming and meditation, also has been observed. His studies have further demonstrated that through meditation and relaxation, it's possible to improve immune function and alleviate and prevent heart disease, stroke and many other chronic health problems.

What's at the heart of sonic healing, says Jonathan Goldman, is vibration. This is backed up by modern physics, which has taught us that all matter – down to the organs of our body – is in a constant state of whirling vibration. "Everything has a unique frequency, or vibration," Goldman explains. "Illness occurs when some sort of contra-vibration intrudes on the normal one. Sound can be used to change these disharmonious frequencies back to normal, healthful vibrations, thereby restoring health."

This physiological principle is known as entrainment: "A phenomenon in which powerful rhythmic vibrations from one source cause less powerful vibrations from another source to lock in step with the more powerful one," says Goldman. "External energy sources, particularly sounds, are especially powerful in affecting our internal rhythms."

Goldman combines his own musical training and intuition to find stagnant energy patterns in a person's vibrational field. By creating a siren-like sound with his voice, he scans a client by directing his voice from the person's feet up to their head, then back down.

Wherever the tone changes, energy is stuck. Goldman then directs the sound at those areas (sometimes holding it in one spot for five minutes or more) until the sound – and hence the person's energy – becomes whole again. A session can last up to an hour and may be accompanied by other healing techniques, such as therapeutic touch.

Don Campbell offers two simple exercises you can try on your own. If you're tired and need some "sonic caffeine", intone a long-e sound (as in emit) for three minutes. You may feel silly for the first minute, he warns, but after the second you'll get into it, and after the third, you'll feel the effects. For a three-minute relaxation, make a long-o (as in ocean) or ah (as in aha) sound.

The research, and healing work, that's being done with sound and music is vast. Campbell, a consultant and trainer to health professionals, musicians and other teachers (he estimates there are 5,000 music therapists working in the United States), explains that much of the work is focused on rehabilitation.

Sound is used as an adjunct therapy in helping people recover from strokes and head injuries. It eases the side effects of chemotherapy – it's especially effective in controlling nausea and pain. In operating rooms it's often used to help relax patients and stabilise their body systems. German studies show that in up to 60 percent of those cases, less anaesthesia is required. Music also has become an increasingly popular therapeutic modality in nursing homes, schools, prisons, day-care centres and spas.

Research shows it to be effective in relieving pain and frustration in people with Alzheimer's, AIDS, autism, trauma, substance abuse, learning disabilities and a host of non-specific physical, emotional and mental impairments. As evidence of how accepted this work has become, Medicare often covers music therapy for patients who have Alzheimer's, are recovering from strokes or learning to walk again.

The work of Mitchell Gaynor, MD, is further proof that sound therapy has infiltrated the mainstream. His credentials are of the highest order: He's the director of medical oncology and integrative medicine at New York's Strang Cancer Prevention Centre, a 66-year-old academic medical centre affiliated with the Cornell Medical Centre, where the Pap smear was invented. In addition to performing conventional cancer treatment (surgery, radiation, chemotherapy), Gaynor runs an ongoing, biweekly support group that utilises guided imagery, meditation and sound, voice and tone.

"Breathing is critical to absolutely everything that produces well-being, yet doctors tend to overlook it," he says. "Besides their vibrational impact, voice and tone are just another way to get the therapeutic value of breathing.

"Five years ago, a Tibetan monk came to see me as a patient," Gaynor continues, "and he gave me a Tibetan bell. The first time I heard that sound, I knew it would change my life."

With the monk's help, Gaynor located some Tibetan "singing" bowls, which are used in many Himalayan cultures to induce meditative states. For the past five years he's been leading his cancer support groups through guided meditations to the sounds created by the Tibetan and quartz-crystal bowls. Though Gaynor hasn't conducted clinical studies to measure the effects of the sound therapy, group members are unanimously thrilled with the results.

"People identify with the bowls' pure tone and have profound relaxation responses," he says. "They tell me that worse than the cancer itself is the fear

Tibetan singing bowls have a profound relaxing effect.

that they have no control over their futures. The relaxation they experience from the sound and meditation makes them more hopeful." Once they have hope, he adds, they often take more active steps towards their healing.

John Ortiz, PhD, a "psycho-musicologist" based in Pennsylvania, is a trained musician and psychologist as well as the author of *The Tao of Music* (1997). He uses a combination of techniques to speed up patients' healing processes.

"Unlike conventional psychotherapy, music is never about why," he says. "It is about who, what, when, where, how. 'Why' can take over a situation and keep you caught up in the analysis instead of taking action."

Ortiz tells the story of a former patient, Charisse Lavelle (name changed for obvious reasons), a 45-year-old marketing executive with a severe case of depression. She had no energy, insomnia, trouble concentrating and had lost interest in her friends and family. She had begun to overeat, which only depressed her more, and she was caught in a vicious cycle. Her MD sent her to a psychiatrist, who put her on antidepressants, which made her inorgasmic and only fuelled the depression. Eventually she found her way to Ortiz.

"Find three songs that sound like your depression, three that feel like you want to feel and three in between," he instructed her. Then he had her make an "entrainment" tape of all nine. She was to fill the rest of the tape with her favourite music.

"Just thinking about it made her mood lift," Ortiz recalls. Since she didn't have all the songs at home, she went to the mall to get the others – something she hadn't done in months. Shopping for the music and making her own tape restored her sense of having some control in her life. Her next tape was music to exercise and dance to, which got her moving again. Within a matter of months of psychological and sound therapy, Charisse was feeling significantly better – and off antidepressants.

What might we expect in the future, then: Tonal spas to rejuvenate our vibrational fields? Chanting centres in schools, workplaces and doctors' offices? Self-teaching CD-ROMs for retoning? Goldman says the possibilities are limitless. When we drum and chant and sing together, feelings of joy and friendship develop. We feel positive and our self-esteem shoots up. And if we're really lucky, we may even have a mystical experience or unleash unrealised creative talents.

More than 50 years ago, Edgar Cayce, the "Sleeping Prophet" who healed thousands of people while in a trance state, said that "music is the medicine of the future". From the sound of things, he was probably right. But hey, that's stale news to the likes of Pythagoras and Confucius!

4. Sound Suggestions

If you'd like to experiment with sound therapy on your own, Ortiz, Campbell and Goldman offer some suggestions.

- Raise your sound awareness by noticing the sounds around you in everyday life. This grounds you in the here and now and enhances your communication skills by improving your listening skills.

- Play your favourite music when you do housework or unpleasant chores. Not only will it distract you, but it will motivate you and create pleasant associations with that activity.

- When you're angry, tense, or frustrated, play an energetic piece of music (such as a march). Move your body for five to seven minutes, letting the music release your emotions. Then your mind can look at the situation with a more objective and compassionate attitude.

- If you want the benefits of deep relaxation but have problems with formal meditation, sit somewhere quiet. Hum or chant different vowel sounds and "direct" them to various parts of your body. When we create and focus on sound, we begin to stop the constant chatter in our minds, which is the first step towards not only deep relaxation, but spiritual enlightenment too!

❑ ❑ ❑

5. Why Music Therapy?

The wife of a man with severe dementia said, "When I was encouraged by a music therapist to sing to my husband, who had been lost in the fog of Alzheimer's disease for so many years, he looked at me and seemed to recognise me. On the last day of his life, he opened his eyes and looked into mine when I sang his favourite hymn. I'll always treasure that last moment we shared together."

Dr Oliver Sacks, at a hearing entitled, "Forever Young: Music and Ageing", stated: "The power of music is very remarkable... One sees Parkinsonian patients unable to walk, but able to dance perfectly well or patients almost unable to talk, who are able to sing perfectly well... I think that music therapy and music therapists are indispensable in institutions for elderly people and among neurologically disabled patients."

A gentleman in the early stages of progressive dementia improvised on a xylophone during a music therapy session to express his feelings, and then stated: "I don't know how anyone can live without music."

A frail 93-year-old woman, referred for music therapy after being diagnosed with major depression, said: "Now, there is no need to be morose. I can have my music here with me and listen to it whenever I want to feel young."

When a couple danced together for the first time after five years of the husband's deterioration from probable Alzheimer's disease, the wife said: "Thank you for helping us dance. It's the first time in three years that my husband held me in his arms." Tearfully, she said that music therapy had made that possible.

❏ ❏ ❏

6. The Multiple Benefits

Music therapy is for anyone. Although it can be used therapeutically for people who have physical, emotional, social, or cognitive deficits, even those who are healthy can use music to relax, reduce stress, improve the mood, or to accompany exercise. There are no potentially harmful or toxic effects.

Music therapists help their patients achieve a number of goals through music, including improvement of communication, academic strengths, attention span, and motor skills. They may also assist with behavioural therapy and pain management.

Physical Effects

The brain function physically changes in response to music. The rhythm can guide the body into breathing in slower, deeper patterns that have a calming effect. Heart rate and blood pressure are also responsive to the types of music that are listened to. The heartbeat tends to speed up or slow down depending on the volume and speed of the auditory stimulus. Louder and faster noises tend to raise both heart rate and blood pressure; slower, softer, and more regular tones produce the opposite result. Music can also relieve muscle tension and improve motor skills. It is often used to help rebuild physical patterning skills in rehabilitation clinics. Levels of endorphins, natural pain relievers, are increased while listening to music, and levels of stress hormones are decreased. This latter effect may partially explain the ability of music to improve immune function.

A 1993 study at Michigan State University showed that even 15 minutes of exposure to music could increase interleukin-1 levels, which heightens immunity.

Mental Effects

Depending on the type and style of sound, music can either sharpen mental acuity or assist in relaxation. Memory and learning can be enhanced. This has been used with good results in children who have learning disabilities. This effect may also be partially due to increased concentration that many people have while listening to music.

Better productivity is another outcome of an improved ability to concentrate. The term "Mozart effect" was coined after a study showed that college students performed better on maths problems when listening to classical music.

Emotional Effects

The ability of music to influence human emotion is well known and is used extensively by moviemakers. A variety of musical moods may be used to create feelings of calmness, tension, excitement, or romance. Lullabies have long been popular for soothing babies to sleep. Music can also be used to express emotion non-verbally – a very valuable therapeutic tool in some settings.

Goals

Music is used to form a relationship with the patient. The music therapist sets goals on an individual basis, depending on the reasons for treatment, and selects specific activities and exercises to help the patient progress. Objectives may include development of communication, cognitive, motor, emotional, and social skills. Some of the techniques used to achieve this are singing, listening, instrumental music, composition, creative movement, guided imagery, and other methods as appropriate.

Other disciplines may be integrated as well, such as dance, art and psychology. Patients may develop musical abilities as a result of therapy, but this is not a major concern. The primary aim is to improve the patient's ability to function.

Techniques

Learning to play an instrument is an excellent musical activity to develop motor skills in individuals with developmental delays, brain injuries, or other motor impairment. It is also an exercise in impulse control and group cooperation. Creative movement is another activity that can help to improve coordination, as well as strength, balance, and gait. Improvisation facilitates the non-verbal expression of emotion. It encourages socialisation and communication about feelings as well.

Singing develops articulation, rhythm, and breath control. Remembering lyrics and melody is an exercise in sequencing for stroke victims and others who may be intellectually impaired. Composition of words and music is one avenue available to assist the patient in working through fears and negative feelings. Listening is an excellent way to practise attending and remembering. It may also make the patient aware of memories and emotions that need to be acknowledged and perhaps talked about. Singing and discussion is a similar method, which is used with some patient populations to encourage dialogue.

Guided Imagery and Music is a very popular technique developed by music therapist Helen Bonny. Listening to music is used as a path to invoke emotions, picture, and symbols from the patient. This is a bridge to the exploration and expression of feelings.

Music and Children

The sensory stimulation and playful nature of music can help develop a child's ability to express emotion, communicate, and develop rhythmic movement. There is also some evidence to show that speech and language skills can be improved through the stimulation of both hemispheres of the brain. Just as with adults, appropriately selected music can decrease stress, anxiety, and pain. Music therapy in a hospital environment with those who are sick, preparing for surgery, or recovering post-operatively, is appropriate and beneficial. Children can also experience improved self-esteem through musical activities that allow them to succeed.

Newborns may enjoy an even greater benefit of music. Those who are premature, experience more rapid weight gain and hospital discharge than their peers who are not exposed to music. There is also anecdotal evidence of improved cognitive function.

The benefits for children include:

- Music therapy enhances the quality of life. It involves relationships between a qualified therapist and child; between one child and another; between child and family; and between the music and the participants. These relationships are structured and adapted through the elements of music to create a positive environment and set the occasion for successful growth.

- Music stimulates all the senses and involves the child at many levels. This "multi-nodal approach" facilitates many developmental skills.

- Quality learning and maximum participation occur when children are permitted to experience the joy of play. The medium of music therapy allows this play to occur naturally and frequently.

- Music is highly motivating, yet it can also have a calming and relaxing effect. Enjoyable music activities are designed to be success-oriented and make children feel better about themselves.

- Music therapy can help a child manage pain and stressful situations.

- Music can encourage socialisation, self-expression, communication, and motor development.

Because the brain processes music in both hemispheres, music can stimulate cognitive functioning and may be used for remediation of some speech/language skills.

Music and Rehabilitation

Patients with brain damage from stroke, traumatic brain injury, or other neurologic conditions have been shown to exhibit significant improvement as a result of music therapy. This is theorised to be partially the result of entrainment, which is the synchronisation of movement with the rhythm of the music. Consistent practice leads to gains in motor skill ability and efficiency. Cognitive processes and language skills often benefit from appropriate musical intervention.

Music and the Elderly

The geriatric population can be especially prone to anxiety and depression, particularly in old home residents. Chronic diseases causing pain are also not uncommon in this setting. Music is an excellent outlet to provide enjoyment, relaxation, relief from pain, and an opportunity to socialise and reminisce about music that has had special importance to the individual.

It can have a striking effect on patients with Alzheimer's disease, even sometimes allowing them to focus and become responsive for a time. Music has also been observed to decrease the agitation that is so common with this disease.

One study shows that elderly people who play a musical instrument are more physically and emotionally fit as they age than their non-musical peers.

Music therapy is efficacious and valid with older persons who have functional deficits in physical, psychological, cognitive or social functioning. Research results and clinical experiences attest to the viability of music therapy even in those who are resistive to other treatment approaches. Music is a form of sensory stimulation, which provokes responses due to the familiarity, predictability, and feelings of security.

Music therapy provides:

- Memory recall – which contributes to reminiscence and satisfaction with life.

- Positive changes in mood and emotional states.

- Sense of control over life through successful experiences.

- Awareness of self and environment which accompanies increased attention to music.

- Anxiety and stress reduction for older adult and caregiver.

- Non-pharmacological management of pain and discomfort.

- Stimulation that provokes interest even when no other approach is effective.

- Structure which promotes rhythmic and continuous movement or vocal fluency as an adjunct to physical rehabilitation.

- Emotional intimacy when spouses and families share creative music experiences.

- Opportunities to interact socially with others.

Music and the Mentally Ill

Music can be an effective tool for the mentally or emotionally ill. Autism is one disorder that has been particularly researched. Music therapy has enabled some autistic children to relate to others and have improved learning skills. Substance abuse, schizophrenia, paranoia, and disorders of personality, anxiety, and affect are all conditions that may be benefited by music therapy.

In these groups, participation and social interaction are promoted through music. Reality orientation is improved. Patients are helped to develop coping skills, reduce stress, and express their feelings.

Music and Hospice

Pain, anxiety, and depression are major concerns with patients who are terminally ill, whether they are in hospice or not. Music can provide some relief from pain, through release of endorphins and promotion of relaxation. It can also provide an opportunity for the patient to reminisce and talk about the fears that are associated with death and dying. Music may help regulate the rapid breathing of a patient who is anxious, and soothe the mind.

Music and Labour

Research has proven that mothers require less pharmaceutical pain relief during labour if they make use of music. Using music that is familiar and associated with positive imagery is the most helpful. During early labour, this will promote relaxation. Maternal movement is helpful to get the baby into a proper birthing position and dilate the cervix.

Enjoying some "music to move by" can encourage the mother to stay active for as long as possible during labour. The rhythmic auditory stimulation may also prompt the body to release endorphins, which are a natural

The right music can ease labour pains and facilitate smooth delivery.

form of pain relief. Many women select different styles of music for each stage of labour, with a more intense, or faster piece feeling like a natural accompaniment to the more difficult parts of labour. Instrumental music is often preferred.

❑ ❑ ❑

7. Treating Alzheimer's Disease

A music therapy programme raised melatonin levels and improved behaviour and sleeping problems in 20 male Alzheimer's patients. Jule Klotter, writing about this path-breaking experiment, says that the Alzheimer's patients underwent music therapy for 30-40 minutes, five days a week for one month. Blood samples were taken before the first session, at the end of the four weeks of therapy, and six weeks after the study's conclusion.

Dr Ardash Kumar and colleagues at the University of Miami School of Medicine (Florida), who reported the study in *Alternative Therapies* (1999), checked the levels of melatonin, norepinephrine, epinephrine, serotonin, and prolactin. These brain chemicals are known to affect the mental state of human beings. They found that melatonin, epinephrine and norepinephrine blood levels had risen significantly by the end of the four-week therapy programme. Moreover, melatonin levels remained high six weeks after the programme had stopped. Epinephrine and norepinephrine levels, by that time, had returned to their original readings. Serotonin and prolactin were not affected by music therapy.

In addition to the hormonal changes, the participants in the study also became more active and cooperative, and slept better.

"Relaxation with the type of music that calms you down is very beneficial," said Kumar. "To promote a sense of calm and well-being, you can listen to your favourite soothing music when you eat, before you sleep, and when you want to relax. **Music** therapy might be a safer and more effective **alternative** to many psychotropic medications. Like meditation and yoga, it can help us maintain our hormonal and emotional balance, even during periods of stress or disease."

❏ ❏ ❏

Part II
AN ESOTERIC SCIENCE

1. Emotions and the Brain

Music is the harmony of the universe in microcosm; for this harmony is life itself; and in man, who is himself a microcosm of the universe, chords and discords are to be found in his pulse, in his heartbeat, his vibration, his rhythm and tone. His health or sickness, his joy or displeasure, shows whether his life has music or not.

–From the Sufi Message of Nazrat Inayat Khan

It is difficult to guess when Homo sapiens first started to use, understand and enjoy music. Many who research the subject believe that music, song and dance preceded language as a means of communication. The unborn child provides some evidence of the capacity of all human beings to react to music when motor responses to rhythmical stimuli, or even specific pieces of music, are commonly reported by the mother.

In the neonatal period, the vocalisations of the young child are musical responses. The rise and fall of the mother's cooing patterns are also very similar in all societies and cultures. As time passed, the musical qualities of rhythm and pitch gradually subsumed into the development of speech. These qualities are subsequently localised mainly in the left side of the brain, which is subject to significant growth between the ages of two and four. This innate capacity of the brain to interpret musical information suggests that the process has some biological survival value too.

Considerable research has proved that there are neurophysical mechanisms, which appear to have an inherent capacity to analyse musical patterns. The rhythms of the body and those of music have also been studied. Changes in pulse rate, respiration, galvanic skin responses and muscle activity have been noted. It has also been proved that the heartbeat could be slowed if the speed of the music was one beat per minute slower than the pulse rate suggesting an entrainment effect between the speed of the music and the pulse.

Music and movement is another area of research. There was a striking increase in muscular activity in the legs in response to dance music, in the forehead in response to an arithmetical task, and in both when loud music was played.

Music is related to certain basic physiological processes. This has been proved scientifically. Music speaks to us. There are ways in which the structure of music can be compared to that of spoken and written language. The study of disturbances of musical function in relation to focal brain damage from strokes and injury has led to the use of the term *amusia* which denotes the impairment of musical skills and understanding associated with a lesion of the cerebral hemisphere. Like aphasia, amusia can be divided into expressive and receptive types. Musical dyslexia and dysgraphia have been used to describe the inability to read or write musical notation respectively.

There is also no doubt that music works as a therapeutic agent. Our response to music lies most obviously in the perception and processing of a series of complex sound waves with powerful emotional overtones. However, music is more than sound, as deaf musicians will testify. Performance is accompanied by movement and body language, both important aspects of communication.

However, not much is known about how the central nervous system registers and reacts to vibrations and particularly those above and below the range of human hearing. The considerable interest and increasing amount of literature on vibro-acoustic therapy, which uses pulsed frequencies of a very low order as well as musical vibrations, suggests that the physical effect of vibration on the nervous system may contribute to the therapeutic potential of music.

Certain musical frequencies vibrate the brain cells and this process might 'wash' the cells so that the cerebrospinal fluid may more effectively carry away the metabolites and waste products of neuronal activity. Maybe, this is the modern equivalent to the ancient belief that the human body and the brain 'resonate' with music.

❑ ❑ ❑

2. Music as Therapy

Music allows us to transcend the everyday states of consci-ousness and travel to places that we either have a memory of or create in our imagination. This process of transcending the mundane evokes psycho physiologic responses when people shift to altered states of consciousness. When an individual uses music for relaxation, their abstract thinking is slowed down as they remain in a normal waking state. As they continue with their process of relaxation, the

Music can take an individual faster into meditative states.

individual moves through the remainder of the six states of consciousness: expanded sensory threshold, daydreaming, trance, meditative states, and rapture.

In these states of consciousness, time takes on a different meaning for the individual. Often during music therapy sessions, people will lose track of time for extended periods, which in turn helps them reduce feelings of stress, anxiety, fear, and pain.

Stress has become, in modern society, the subject of many best-selling books and is often a lead story in the daily papers. Non-invasive and easily accessible ways to deal with stress have now become critical issues. People need to be educated about the remedial effects of music as therapy.

Many still feel that music used as therapy is just another liberal health fad. Despite this belief, music therapy continues to be a growing occupation. There are more than 5,000 certified and licensed music therapists in the United States working in hospitals, rehabilitation units, health-care and educational settings. The American Music Therapy Association now recognises 68 schools in the United States who offer programmes of study in music therapy.

Music therapy is a non-verbal type of therapy, as opposed to other types of therapy where the client talks about feelings and experiences of life. Music therapy presents an alternative to traditional types of therapy, and provides the following benefits to patients:

- More direct access to thinking and feeling states.

- Opportunity to "contain" feelings for periods of time so that these can be explored, examined, and worked through for the individual.

- Non-verbal expression of thinking and feeling states that are not yet within the verbal domain for the individual.

- Elicitation of imagery and associations that are not accessible through verbal means.

- More direct physiological benefits for the individual than verbal methods.

- Freedom to explore and try out various solutions to patient thinking and feeling problems through exploration and creativity.

There are many applications of music therapy in our everyday lives and the fields of treatment are very broad, encompassing psycho-therapeutic, educational, instructional, behavioural, pastoral, supervisory, healing, recreational, activity, and interrelated arts applications.

Barbara Crowe, past President of the National Association of Music Therapy in the United States, suggests that music and rhythm create their healing effects by calming the constant chatter of the left brain. "A loud repetitive sound sends a constant signal to the cortex, masking input from other senses like vision, touch, and smell," she explains.

When sensory input is decreased, the normally noisy left brain with its internal conversations, analyses, and logical judgements subsides to a murmur, stimulating deeper parts of the brain that are throne-rooms of symbols, visualisation and emotions. "This is the seat of ritual in tribal societies," she observes. "There is a clear, distinct parallel between traditional shamanism and the practices we do in music therapy today."

Raymond Bahr, Director of Coronary Care at St Agnes Hospital, Baltimore, contends without a doubt that music therapy ranks high on the list of modern-day management of critical care patients... Its relaxing properties enable patients to get well faster by allowing them to accept their condition and treatment without excessive anxiety.

❏ ❏ ❏

3. Music as Medicine

Music enters the body through the ear, and the bones of the body act like a tuning fork. The neurological fields of the body are then stimulated by music. Music is a means by which all people can feel these healing vibrations. Even people with profound handicaps can benefit from music healing effects. Research in physiological responses to music supports the hypothesis that listening to music influences a person's autonomic responses.

Science has proven that music focused in the higher register increases tension. Conversely, music played in the lower register reduces tension. Music that is played at a tempo of 80-90 beats per minute increases tension, while music played at 40-60 beats per minute decreases tension.

According to Dr Arthur Harvey, there are four distinct ways in which our brain responds to music: cognitive, affective, physical, and transpersonal. When music is used as medicine, it is used in a way that directly affects the health of the patient. An example is the use of music in "audio-analgesia". Music is used in this way to alleviate or lessen pain, and can be used, at times, in lieu of pain medications. When music is used in this way, it is a necessary component in affecting the outcome of the treatment.

Vibrational therapy sessions can be used to affect physiological changes such as lowering of blood pressure, heart rate, and muscle tension. Studies have shown that music used as medicine can increase the immune function and decrease ACTH (stress) hormones. Music and sound has also been shown to kill cancer cells.

Another benefit of "healing" music is to stir our emotions and feelings, to help us deal with grief, sadness, anger or other feelings. By allowing ourselves to really experience the feelings, the intensity will eventually lessen and even dissipate, resulting in healing. When we avoid our feelings (consciously or subconsciously) they nonetheless tend to build up inside. They don't just go away. Music and sound are wonderful tools for helping us deal with feelings within us, whether we're aware of them or not.

Types of Healing Music

After all that has been said, we may ask ourselves what type of music is healing? Music that energises our body, stimulates our brain, awakens our feelings, ignites our soul, relaxes our body, calms our mind, unwinds our emotions, motivates our actions, helps us unwind, helps us sleep, wakes us up, expands our thinking, and helps us not to think, all of these can be healing.

Music used in the appropriate way can be healing. The key is to use wisdom and listen to what our inner healer tells us about how music makes us feel. There is no one type of music that is healing music. Listen to a wide variety of music and pay attention to how you respond with your whole being (mind, body, and spirit). Large listings of music are available all over the world for various illnesses, situations of the mind and other purposes.

By no means are these the only pieces of music that are healing, and the lists may change dramatically over time as more and more people become involved in this exciting field of health and healing. Music, of course, cannot replace sound medical advice. Music can uphold the emotion, the spirit and the soul and can benefit anybody, whatever the situation. But it is erroneous to believe that it is a panacea.

❏ ❏ ❏

4. Riddle of the Mozart Effect

You must hand it to the Chinese. They never fail to use body parts whatever the occasion! Now they are producing musical albums with some curious titles. Obesity and Constipation are two. Insomnia is another. There's Liver, Heart, and Lungs, and also an orchestral piece that has been nicknamed The Kidney Bladder Suite by Don Campbell, a trained classical musician, composer, and author. Most of the albums use traditional Chinese instruments and are flawlessly performed. The Chinese "take" these musical compositions like they'd take a herbal medicine, to help them get over the problems described in the album titles, or strengthen the organs named in the titles.

The Japanese aren't far behind too. On a visit to Japan, Campbell says he came across more compilations of classical and romantic music with prescriptive suggestions. For headaches and migraines, the Japanese suggested Mendelssohn's *Spring Song*, Dvorak's *Humoresque*, or even a dose of George Gershwin's *An American in Paris*.

Music therapy is an ancient science. In hospitals throughout India, traditional Indian music is used medicinally. In Chennai, in the south of India, the Raga Research Centre has assembled an interdisciplinary team of doctors who experiment with different ragas for use in music therapy. They have found two particular ragas beneficial in treating hypertension and mental illness.

This is nothing new, really. The roots of shamanic and indigenous music reach back to the dawn of civilisation,

45

when the sound of the drum, rattle, and other primitive instruments would bring communities together, launch crop plantings and harvests, and march tribes into battle. People believed that music and sound magically allowed the powers above and below to come together.

Humans, we have to assume, have known ever since they took to singing or played their first musical instrument (a bone flute between 43,000 and 82,000 years ago) that music evokes powerful forces. Evidence even suggests that dance and song preceded speech, which means that music is humanity's original language. Researchers, in fact, have found that two-thirds of the inner ear's cilia – thousands of tiny hair that lie on a flat plane like piano keys – resonate only at the higher "musical" frequencies (3,000 to 20,000 hertz). This would seem to tell us that at one time human beings communicated primarily through song or tone.

Modern scientists agree that many different kinds of music can be therapeutic. Some people respond well to reggae or jazz. Others are uplifted – indeed healed – after listening to Gregorian chants, or heavy metal. But researchers have discovered that the work of one composer in particular – Wolfgang Amadeus Mozart – mysteriously rises above all other forms of music in its power to heal the human body. This special ability of Mozart's music to heal is called the *Mozart Effect.* Scientists are not only beginning to understand that some forms of music are more healing than others, with Mozart's at the top, but they're also starting to understand why.

Stammering Depardieu

Alfred Tomatis, MD, a celebrated French physician, has spent five decades studying the healing and creative powers of sound and music, the Mozart Effect in particular. Many of his patients call him Dr Mozart. Tomatis has tested more than 100,000 clients in his listening centres throughout the world for listening disabilities and vocal and auditory handicaps, as well as learning disorders.

One of his better-known patients was Gerard Depardieu, the French actor. Many moviegoers have heard Depardieu speak with a mellifluous voice, but in the mid-1960s, he was a tongue-tied young man still struggling to become an actor. Coming from a background of family difficulties, educational failures, and personal sorrows, Depardieu could not express himself. In fact, he could hardly speak coherently. And the more he tried, the worse his stammering became.

French actor Gerard Depardieu's stammer was cured through music therapy.

A drama teacher directed him to the Tomatis Centre in Paris, where he met with Tomatis himself. Tomatis diagnosed the cause of Depardieu's voice and memory difficulties as deeper emotional problems underlying his physiological difficulties and said that he could help him. Depardieu asked what the treatment would involve – surgery, medication, or speech therapy. Tomatis responded, "For the next several weeks, I want you to come here every day for two hours and listen to Mozart."

"Mozart?" Depardieu asked, puzzled.

"Mozart," Tomatis repeated.

The next day Depardieu returned to the Tomatis Centre to don headphones and listen to Mozart. After only a few sessions, he began to experience positive changes in his daily routine. His appetite improved, he slept better, and he found himself with more energy. Soon, he was speaking more clearly. After several months, Depardieu returned to acting school with new poise and confidence, and went on to become one of the consummate actors of his generation.

"Before Tomatis," Depardieu says, looking back, "I could not complete any of my sentences. He helped give continuity to my thoughts, and he gave me the power to synthesise and understand what I was thinking."

Tomatis found again and again that regardless of a listener's tastes or previous exposure to the composer, the music of Mozart invariably calmed listeners, improved spatial perception, and allowed them to express themselves more clearly. He found that Mozart indisputably achieved the best results, long term, whether in Tokyo, Cape Town, or Amazonia.

Little Krissy

In recent years, the music of Mozart (1756–1791) has become part of many doctors' pharmacopoeia as they've seen patients rebound under its influence. Krissy, for example, weighed just over one-and-a-half pounds when she was born prematurely in a Chicago hospital with a life-threatening condition. Doctors put her on total life support. Other than an occasional pat on the head, the only positive stimulation she received was from constant infusions of Mozart that her mother begged nurses to pipe into the neonatal unit. Doctors did not think Krissy would live; her mother, however, believes that the Mozart Effect saved her daughter's life.

Krissy could not sit up at age one and did not walk until she was two. Her motor skills were poor, and she was anxious and introverted. Despite all this, at age three she tested far ahead of her years in abstract reasoning. One evening, her parents took Krissy to a chamber music concert. For days afterward, she played with an empty tube from a paper towel roll, which she placed under her chin like an instrument, and she bowed "with a chopstick".

Her mother enrolled Krissy in Suzuki violin lessons, and the four-year-old could immediately reproduce from memory pieces seemingly several levels beyond her physical ability. With the support of her parents, teachers, and fellow students, Krissy stopped wringing her hands in fear and began to socialise.

In the past several years, many stories like Krissy's have emerged. Music is apparently healing more and more people.

While we all know intuitively that music can alter our mood, the enhancing effects of music on creativity, learning, and health have become known to researchers around the world. And Mozart's music, in particular, is getting a strong thumbs-up from scientists:

- In monasteries in Brittany, monks play music to the animals in their care and have found that cows serenaded with Mozart give more milk.
- In Washington State, Department of Immigration and Naturalisation officials play Mozart and baroque music during English classes for new arrivals from Cambodia, Laos, and other Asian countries and report that it speeds up their learning.
- The city of Edmonton, Alberta, Canada, pipes Mozart string quartets into the city squares to calm pedestrian traffic. Officials found, in addition to other benefits, drug dealings have lessened.
- In northern Japan, Ohara Brewery finds that when Mozart is played near yeast, that yeast makes the best sake. The density of yeast used for brewing the traditional rice wine – a measure of quality – increases by a factor of ten when the yeast "listen" to Mozart.

The power of Mozart's music came to public attention largely through innovative research at the University of California in the mid-1990s. At the Centre for the Neurobiology of Learning and Memory in Irvine, a research team began to look at the effects of Mozart on college students and children. Frances H. Rauscher, PhD, and her colleagues conducted a study in which 36 undergraduates from the psychology department scored eight to nine points higher on the spatial IQ test after listening to ten minutes of Mozart's *Sonata for Two Pianos in D Major.*

Mozart's music "may 'warm up' the brain", suggested Gordon Shaw, a theoretical physicist and one of the Irvine researchers. He suspects that complex music facilitates certain complex neuronal patterns involved in high brain activities like maths and chess. By contrast, simple and repetitive music could have the opposite effect.

In a follow-up study, the scientists explored the neurophysiological bases of this enhancement. Spatial intelligence was further tested by projecting 16 abstract figures similar to folded pieces of paper on an overhead screen for one minute each. The exercises tested whether 79 students could tell how the items would look when they were unfolded. Over a five-day period, one group listened to the original Mozart sonata, another to silence, and a third to mixed sounds, including the music of Philip Glass, an audiotaped story, and a dance piece.

The researchers reported that all three groups improved their scores from day one to day two, but the Mozart group's pattern recognition soared 62 percent compared to 14 percent for the silence group and 11 percent for the mixed-sound group. The Mozart group continued to achieve the highest scores on subsequent days.

Proposing a mechanism for this effect, the scientists suggested that listening to Mozart helps "organise" the firing patterns of neurons in the cerebral cortex, especially strengthening creative right-brain processes associated with spatial-temporal reasoning. Listening to music, they concluded, acts as "an exercise" for facilitating operations associated with higher brain function. In plain English, it can improve your concentration and enhance your ability to make intuitive leaps.

Following the Irvine studies, a number of public schools introduced Mozart pieces as background music and reported improvements in their pupils' attention and performance. The Mozart Effect is real!

❏ ❏ ❏

5. How Does Music Heal?

To understand how music in general can heal – and why Mozart is particularly therapeutic for many people – one must understand sound and its effect on physical matter. In the book *Cymatics*, Hans Jenny, a Swiss engineer and doctor, describes the science of how sound and vibration interact with matter. Jenny shows that intricate geometric figures can be formed by sound. For instance, Jenny has created vibrations in crystals with electrical impulses and transmitted the vibrations to a medium such as a plate or a string. He has also produced oscillating figures in liquids and gases.

The forms and shapes that can be created by sound are infinite and can be varied simply by changing the pitch, the harmonics of the tone, and the material that is vibrating. When chords are added, the result can be either beauty or chaos. A low Aum sound, for example, produces a few concentric circles with a dot at their centre and a high EEE many circles with wobbly edges. These forms change instantaneously when a different note or tone is sounded.

Imagine what effect sounds have on delicate cells, tissues, and organs. Vibrating sounds form patterns and create energy fields of resonance and movement in the surrounding space. We absorb these energies, and they subtly alter our breath, pulse, blood pressure, muscle tension, skin temperature, and other internal rhythms. Jenny's discoveries help us understand how, like a potter shaping clay at her wheel, sound shapes and sculpts us both inside and out.

It's also been partly through the work of Linda Rodgers that scientists and physicians have become aware that the vibrations transmitted by music can positively affect a patient, or negatively affect the patient if it's the wrong music for that patient. A clinical social worker and classically trained musician from New York, Rodgers became interested in the effects of music on surgical patients in the wake of a traumatic tonsillectomy she underwent as a child. She had become highly sensitive to the anxiety that can erupt in the face of surgery and the need to somehow defuse it.

In 1982, Rodgers went to work at Mount Sinai Hospital in New York and obtained permission to watch open-heart surgery. There she began to investigate patients' ability to hear under anaesthesia. She soon uncovered a wealth of research indicating that they do continue to hear, even when rendered unconscious. One of the classic experiments involved an anaesthetised cat whose EEG channels all dramatically responded to the barking of a dog. "The auditory pathway, unlike all other sensory systems, has an extra relay," Rodgers explains. "Auditory fibres are not affected by anaesthetics, so they continue to transmit sound. Simply stated: We never stop hearing!" And our conscious participation is not needed.

Rodgers has successfully implemented music protocols in operating rooms. To protect against patients inadvertently hearing harmful noise or tasteless (and possibly injurious) remarks – such as "This old bag won't make it" – during surgery, Rodgers recommends that audiotapes selected by each patient be played before, during, and after surgery on cassette players with earphones.

Rodgers says that as patients learn to invoke music's powers, "It is reasonable to expect a more rapid recovery from surgery, with fewer complications, reduced number of days in the hospital, and a more positive response to coping with future medical problems."

❏ ❏ ❏

6. What's So Special About Mozart?

Why not call the transformative powers of music the Bach Effect, the Beethoven Effect, or the Beatles Effect? Does Mozart's music have unique properties, eliciting universal responses that only now are yielding to measurement?

Mozart doesn't weave a dazzling tapestry like that of the great mathematical genius Bach. He doesn't raise tidal waves of emotions like the epically tortured Beethoven. He doesn't soothe the body like a good folk musician or slam it into motion like a rock star.

However, he is at once deeply mysterious and accessible. His wit, charm, and simplicity allow us to locate a deeper wisdom in ourselves. Tomatis asserts that Mozart's "music has a liberating, healing power which exceeds by far what we observe in his predecessors, ...his contemporaries, or his successors".

To many listeners, Mozart's music seems to impart balance. If it indeed imparts energetic balance – and we do know that it, like all sound, changes the energy of our bodies in specific ways – then Mozart's music is doing what many systems of healing strive to do. Whether through acupuncture, herbal medicines, dietary planning, or assorted other measures, many systems of healthcare seek to help the patient find energetic balance. Mozart's music may be energy-balancing extraordinaire. It's not too fast, or too slow. Somehow it's "just right".

The rhythms of music, we know, affect the rhythms of the autonomic nervous system, which regulates a vast biological landscape within our bodies. We can understand, therefore, how important the simplicity and clarity of Mozart's music may be to our emotional and physical bodies.

One can liken the effects of different music to the effects of different foods, which also have the power to alter energy patterns and change our physiology, for both good and bad. A spicy Chinese meal, or a sweet dessert, each will affect us – temperamentally and physically – much differently than a fruit salad. With foods, a steady diet of the most delicious and sensuous is not necessarily the best for us. Sometimes it's the simple tastes that serve us best on a regular basis.

So it may be with music. We are likely fed well by a variety of music, but some forms are more likely to bring order and stability to our emotions. Tomatis is convinced that Mozart's music is exceptional at bringing harmony to body and mind.

Gerard Depardieu, whose speech difficulties were healed by listening to Mozart, actually listened to Mozart that had been "filtered". It had certain frequencies taken out and others amplified according to Depardieu's specific needs. Some people do not hear certain frequencies as well as they should and they end up with "deficiencies" in these frequencies. By "feeding" the patient these frequencies, the deficiencies are corrected.

Tomatis uses Mozart because it filters better than any other kind of music. You could liken the filtered frequencies to "sonic vitamins", or "sound nutrients". They were the specific frequencies, or vibrational nutrition, that Depardieu required. Tomatis has found that Mozart, better than any other kind of music, is a nutritionally balanced musical meal and it is easier to filter out needed frequencies from his compositions than from other composers.

Wolfgang Amadeus Mozart, the child prodigy who wrote operas, symphonies, piano concertos, piano sonatas, and music for organ, clarinet, and other instruments by the time he was 12 years old, may have left the world a library of the most delicious healing sounds yet discovered.

❏ ❏ ❏

7. More on Healing Music

Since the beginning of recorded history, music has played a significant role in the healing of humankind, writes Amrita Cottrell, who has researched the subject with immense care. Music and healing were communal activities natural to everyone. In ancient Greece, Apollo was both the god of music and medicine. Ancient Greeks said, "Music is an art imbued with power to penetrate into the very depths of the soul." These beliefs were shared through their Doctrine of

Plato believed that music was "the essence of order".

Ethos. In the mystery schools of Egypt and Greece, healing and sound were considered a highly developed sacred science.

Plato shared this profound belief: "Music is a moral law. It gives soul to the universe, wings to the mind, flight to the imagination, a charm to sadness, gaiety and life to everything. It is the essence of order, and leads to all that is good, just, and beautiful, of which it is the invisible, but nevertheless dazzling, passionate and eternal form."

New Age guru Deepak Chopra has beautifully written, "Where is music? You can find it at many levels in the vibrating strings, the trip of the hammers, the fingers striking the keys, the black marks on the paper, or the nerve impulses produced in the player's brain. But all of these are just codes; the reality of music is the shimmering, beautiful, invisible

55

form that haunts our memories without ever being present in the physical world."

Goldman and Gurin's work on psycho-immunology revealed that nerve fibres are contained in every organ of the immune system, which provide biological communication between the nerve endings and the immune system. They postulate that there is a direct link between a person's thoughts, attitudes, perceptions, and emotions, and the health of the immune system. This being the case, we have the ability to be proactive in the health of our bodies and minds.

Music is a way to tap into the innate knowledge that resides deep in our cells. We live "in" music. Great music nourishes us in ways we don't even realise. It inspires us, relaxes us, energises us – in short, it heals us and keeps us well. It resides everywhere in our world. While we may not always be listening to a Beethoven Symphony or a Mozart Sonata, the cosmos is a tonal harmony of many sounds interacting and vibrating together. Music is the pulse of the energy that courses in and through everything via vibrations.

Don Campbell, the music aficionado, says that music can be delicate and quiet, but never sedentary. Even a tone that extends for hours at a time, unvarying, carries a pulsing wave that affects our mind and body at many levels. What we bring to each sound is also of vital importance. He goes on to say, "You, the listener, determine the final impact: You are an active conductor and participant in the process of orchestrating health."

❑ ❑ ❑

8. The Power of Chant and Toning

Music of many different genres can help enhance the mind/body connection. Healing mantras, chants, and incantations have ancient and obscure origins but are seen throughout history and in every major world culture – Hinduism, Muslim, Judaism, Native American, Polynesian, Asian, Sufi, etc. The power of chant involves bridging the two worlds of humanity and eternity. It allows a person to touch a deeper world that is organic and flowing. Chant has no set rhythm and is based on the breath in combination with tonal patterns of sustained vowels.

Toning is a powerful form of chant with many definitions. Laurel Elizabeth Keyes, forerunner of toning as a healing art, and author of *Toning: The Creative Power of the Voice*, says, "Toning is an ancient method of healing… the idea is simply to restore people to their harmonic patterns."

Don Campbell describes toning as, "Simple and audible sound, prolonged long enough to be identified. Toning is the conscious elongation of a sound using the breath and voice."

John Beaulieu, author of *Music and Sound in the Healing Arts* says, "Toning is the simple and natural process of making vocal sounds for the purpose of balance… toning sounds are sounds of expression and do not have a precise meaning."

Keyes recounts the time when she first started to experiment with toning. She said that it was more than just a release of tension. When she allowed the tones to emerge without trying to control them, she experienced a cleansing of her whole body.

Toning and chant have been making their way into mainstream culture over the last 20 years. *Chant*, the popular recording from the early 1990 by the Benedictine Monks of Santo Domingo de Silos, Spain, sold over 4 million copies in 42 countries by the spring of 1994. These monks have committed themselves to a lifestyle that is based on cycles. Others do not experience these cycles in the world in the same way. The cycles revolve around the sacred liturgy of the Roman Catholic Church, and include an intricate series of interlocking patterns within the organisation. By submitting themselves to these cycles, the monks actually become part of this great tapestry of history and sound.

Katherine Lee Mee, producer of the CD, says about this recording, "Time seems to stop. The darting mind falls still and attentive, arrested from its worldly concerns and preoccupations... like fire, each line has its own brightness and energy, a force that is called forth, raised and then surrendered. Like water, the music rises and falls in a gentle wave of love that bathes, cleanses, and caresses our spirits, leaving us buoyed up and restored."

The *San Francisco Examiner* music critic said this about *Chant*, "What we're talking about is inner peace, transcendence, a serenity, beyond mortal care. For a generation that frowns on organised religious movements (or organised anything), this is, without a doubt, the new soul music."

Powerful effective responses to music can be witnessed in the lives of spiritual masters. Their physical health reflects their spiritual health as well. They experience this power through practising the art of music and chant as a means of obtaining spiritual enlightenment.

Where did the ancient chants originate? Were they evolved from logical thought processes that were later transferred to a musical format? Or rather, were they birthed from those who had learned to harness the healing powers of their spirit, and given expression through their spiritual practice to bring the ecstatic experience into vocal and instrumental form through music?

❏ ❏ ❏

9. How Music Affects Us

How does music affect our well-being? It seems there is no definitive answer to this question. However, experts in the field of music and sound therapy feel there are two major ways in which music and sound can affect our lives.

The first is the principle of entrainment. This refers to the phenomena of being in sync. In other words, our bodies automatically adjust to the pace, rhythm, or pulse of the music. How many times have you walked into a room with other things on your mind and heard music playing? You stop to listen for a few minutes and all of a sudden, your foot is tapping to the music or you are swaying your head or body with the beat. Or, a certain piece of music evokes memories of a time when you heard the music before, and the feelings of that time come immediately back into your awareness. In scientific terms, our psyches and bodies become entrained to the sonic environment created by the music.

Entrainment is a powerful tool in behaviour modification. In effect, the principle of entrainment directly relates to the Greek word *isomorphic* (commonly referred to as the iso principle). Isomorphic means *same form* or appearance. Therefore, musical entrainment is actually a process of joining with feelings conveyed in the music and sensing the feeling of commonality with it. One might almost have an experience of feeling a connection with the composer or performer by sharing emotions and feelings conveyed in the music, either through its creation or through the performance itself.

Music in this sense can be a powerful tool in both positive and negative ways to the listener. Music entrainment is more than just a tool to be used for behaviour modification, however. Music has the power to integrate the whole person allowing profound healing on many levels.

Music is one of the few experiences that can touch a person on all levels of consciousness. It is a powerful sensory stimulus that can work simultaneously on the body, mind, and spirit. Vibrational entrainment, as a result of listening to music, can bring harmony to the body by actually entraining the body with the music. It can have a transformative effect on an individual by moving through the body systems and bringing about harmony. Through the use of music, positive effects have been seen in the nervous system, affecting the endocrine system, which in turn enhances the immune system.

For centuries shamans have used drums and vocal sounds as an integral part of healing practices in indigenous cultures. They often went into a trance themselves through the power of music, which they used as a tool in assisting the healing process.

Music for Diversion

A second principle that music utilises in affecting patients is the principle of diversion. This method of utilising music and sound is helpful in taking the attention away from an unpleasant or unwanted situation. An example of diversionary music is the playing of bright, happy, energising music when the listener feels down in the dumps. Music, in this sense, can be used in a therapeutic situation to reduce anxiety and pain, temporarily transporting the listener to another reality during the healing process.

The International Association of Pain has defined pain as "an unpleasant sensory and emotional experience associated with actual or potential tissue damage". In other words, pain is a symptom of disharmony. Pain can be viewed as a series of sounds or vibrations that send messages to the brain indicating a disharmony in some part of the body. Think of this vibration as an alarm sounding to warn of a problem in the body. The mind and body can be re-programmed to a place of harmony and healing by entraining it with music.

❏ ❏ ❏

10. Sound, Rhythm and Music

There are a number of researchers currently working with sound looking to effect a change in the physical body and/or the etheric field. There are many sound healing concepts such as: using "missing" frequencies in the person's voice; using the voice in a harmonic toning way; human energy centre (chakra) correlation, and the use of brain/body synchronisation frequencies – to name a few.

Harmonic resonance is a way to restore balance, harmony and vitality by offering music and sounds that resonate with you in such a way as to present a musical model of you in your optimal, vibrational, and resonant state. As our society becomes more information oriented, we are looking for more validation of these phenomena.

You can formulate your own set of guidelines about how to use music in a positive way and, to use sound and music in a way that can restore balance and harmony into all aspects of your life. This can result in improved health, vitality, emotional stability, and a heightened state of consciousness and awareness. This is an opportunity to truly be "in the present". This comes through clearing the "emotional baggage", the old wounds (fear, guilt, self-doubt, anger, shame, rage, obsessions and so on) that many of us seem to carry around from time to time. Sometimes it becomes such a deep part of our personalities that it runs us rather than "us" being totally free to be who we truly are.

How Does Sound Work?

A sound wave basically causes changes in air pressure as it moves through the air. Our ears respond to this information and our brain processes it into sound information. Stand in front of a good speaker playing low bass or hold your hand under a large drum being played and you'll feel the air currents moving. We also receive sound information from our whole bodies. Our skin is very tactile and responds to sound waves quite readily.

Sound and music are separate. Sound is just that – a sound. It may or may not have a pitch (specific frequency) or a pure waveform or a temporal (rhythmic) pattern but if it's audible or perceptible, we call it a sound. Music is a combining of elements that typically incorporates these sounds into a lyrical blend of pitch, melody and rhythm and progresses/modulates from one chord to another in an emotional fashion. Combinations of pitches/chords/intervals that are perceived as being harmonious and pleasant are described as being consonant. Harsh combinations are called dissonant.

It is often very important and appropriate to use dissonance of varying degrees in healing music. If you are stuck, sometimes you need a bit of a push to move on, and if the musical environment is kept too sweet and cheery then you don't have much incentive to journey forward.

Generally, major keys are perceived as being light and uplifting. Minor keys are felt as being more serious, reverent, and mysterious.

11. Harmonic Resonance

John Oliver is an Associate Composer of the Canadian Music Centre and co-director of Earsay Productions.

He came to international attention during 1988/89 when he won six prizes for five compositions ranging from chamber to orchestral to electroacoustic music.

Based in Vancouver, Canada, John Oliver writes music for acoustic and electronic instruments. His recent music combines familiar musical materials or techniques with new inventions, with a view to creating a new, exciting listening experience.

John Oliver believes music has a profound influence on the human body.

John began piano study at the age of five. One of the first things he noticed was that certain notes on the piano would make certain objects in the room buzz consistently. One note made the teacups on the shelf buzz, another would make the picture frame over the sofa buzz, another made the storm windows rattle.

"This was my first exposure to resonance; technically called sympathetic vibration (I call it Harmonic Resonance™). Gently depressing and holding the middle C key on the piano without making the hammer hit the string (thus making the string vibrate) and then sharply hitting the C below middle C would make the middle C string vibrate," John says.

He later saw some pictures in a book called *Cymatics* by Dr Hans Jenny. Basically, Dr Jenny took a speaker or transducer and attached it to either a membrane or thin plate of steel and covered this with a variety of substances such as iron filings, silica powder, milk, and water. Smoke-filled chambers were also used. He then played a specific frequency into the speaker or transducer and photographed the results. The particles formed incredible patterns with remarkable similarities to naturally occurring patterns, which ranged from moonscape-like images to mandalas (complex symbols used in Buddhist meditation) to stalagmite-looking forms. As the frequency was changed, the forms and patterns changed.

"I thought that the human body must respond this way as well," he says. "We are about 90% water (fluid), our bones are great conductors of vibration and we have a variety of densities provided by tissue mass, fat, muscle, organs and bones (skeletal system). Given how profoundly sound affects these material substances, it is easy to understand how our body and spirit takes on the patterns of music."

John continues. "While pondering the nature of the universe and the essence of life, I came to the conclusion that everything is vibrational in nature. In matter, there is an atomic structure with a nucleus with electrons and protons circling in a specific, 'harmonic-resonant' pattern. Thinking of disease I reasoned that disease is 'dis-ease', 'dis-harmony', 'dis-sonance', 'dis-illusion', 'dis-connection' (fragmentation of the psyche). They are synonymous for the same thing – not being whole, connected and integrated.

"I did considerable research with a number of massage and alternative health practitioners. Using kinesiology, acupuncture pulses, and other testing methods, a capable practitioner can do an assessment of everything from metabolic function to emotional involvement. We then find the specific frequency (pitch) and waveform (instrument) which, when played, will restore balance to the area affected.

"Muscles which tested very weak before the music treatment – a little finger can sometimes push down the entire arm or leg – often show remarkable changes in strength and muscle reflex response. They become so strong that while the tones are playing, you can lift yourself off the ground using the same previously weak muscles. This tells you that the sound is doing something very profound. I then compose a 30-to-45-minute long piece of music based on the specific frequencies and waveforms that demonstrate the balancing and vitalising responses. The specific sounds address the specific areas, but the combination of the sounds into 'music' is what gets the emotions involved. Allowing for an emotional and soul-level healing creates the opportunity for a complete physical body healing."

The client receives a CD or tape of their custom music to play for themselves regularly for ongoing benefits. One client was scheduled for a series of root canal procedures in two teeth. He was so sensitive to the analgesic drugs typically used to manage the pain that he was concerned. "I said I'd make him a tape of sounds and music that would numb his tooth and displace the pain," says John. "We found the frequencies of the affected teeth and then found the frequencies of certain acupuncture points that provided an outlet for the pain. It worked and we were on to something."

John pauses and continues, "Experiments showed that we respond to sounds that we cannot hear. We put the selected sounds exclusively into a pair of headphones and put them on a person's ankles. They responded to the sound even though their ears could not 'hear' the sound. Once you vibrate a part of the body the blood cells carry this resonance to the whole body very quickly. Research done with deaf children also showed that the children could identify different sounds and instruments by laying on a giant membrane and having the sounds played through it."

❏ ❏ ❏

12. Different Music Therapy Methods

Not yet a systematised discipline, there are different methods to approach music therapy. These include:

Improvisational Music Therapy

The improvisational model often includes Nordoff-Robbins, Clinical Orff Schulwerk, or other types of improvisational styles. The basic philosophy of improvisational music therapy is that these techniques elicit a client's response from every level. It develops contact with the client within the context of the musical experience. The role of a music therapist in this model often works supportively, creating a musical emotional environment that accepts and enhances the client's responses. This method provides experiences for socialisation, communication, and expression of feelings and emotions among group participants.

The most common instruments used for this method are rhythm instruments and Orff instruments. The music therapist can also integrate movement, speech, and drama in this model.

Singing and Discussion

Singing and discussion is a typical music therapy method that can be used for adolescent populations as well as for the elderly. The music stimulates clients' responses to the lyric parts. Sometimes the music itself encourages the expression of thoughts and feelings associated with the songs.

Typical procedures of this method are as follows: The therapist usually opens the session by singing songs familiar to the clients. After singing several songs, the therapist leads a discussion related to the themes of the songs. Once each client has expressed and discussed his or her own thoughts, feelings, and ideas, the therapist improvises a song with the words from the clients.

This can be a very positive conclusion to the session (in fact, the therapist makes a song to be positive) so that each client might carry over his or her feelings and emotions in productive ways.

Guided Imagery and Music

GIM or Guided Imagery and Music is a technique in which the act of listening to classical music is combined with a relaxed state of mind and body in order to evoke imagery for the purpose of self-actualisation. The imagery evoked reflects aspects of the self and is used by the client, with the aid of the therapist.

GIM does not intend to cure or treat symptoms; rather, it is in search of the client's inner awareness. There is a belief that everyone can understand his or her problems and has the ability to overcome the problem within the self. Thus, GIM is based on humanistic therapy, influenced by Abraham Maslow and Jung.

Clinical Orff Schulwerk

This approach, utilising the method of music education developed by Carl Orff for German school children, has been specially adapted for mentally retarded and autistic children in the United States. COS or Clinical Orff Schulwerk offers an effective groundwork for these children because of their pre-disposition toward rhythm, order and repetition.

The overall process involves the use of movement, rhythm, sounds, language and musical expression in a group experience. Structure is provided by simple chants, rondos, poems, nonsense words and ostinati employed, all sung within the pentatonic scale. The rondo form is used extensively, as it allows for repetition as well as for individual creative response.

Specially-designed percussion instruments permit the participation of even the most severely disturbed or handicapped child. Through "successive approximation", specific tasks are taught in a concrete step-by-step approach. Learning is effected through modelling (imitation) and behaviour shaping, reinforced by behavioural techniques. With groups of autistic children, considerable attention is given to language development through the use of sign language, which is seen as enhancing speech.

Among other areas dealt with in the Orff context are body image and awareness, laterality, gross motor expression, fine motor coordination, receptive language, spatial relationships, simple categorising and simple association. The significant value of COS is that it helps the child become invested in a meaningful group experience.

❑ ❑ ❑

13. Six Tips for Using Music in Therapy & Education

1. Use Silence

Once we know a piece of music, we notice when it is interrupted. You can use unexpected pauses in music to get the attention of students whose attention has wandered. Once you have their attention back, you can resume exactly where you left off – like the pause button on a tape recorder. No verbal cues necessary, just silence.

2. Make Sure the Lyrics Fit the Music

When you are using songs to teach academic concepts – especially to students with language delays – be sure that the words and phrases in the song are pronounced as they would be in speech. Often, when songs are "piggybacked" (new words with a familiar melody) the words get distorted. Many children with special needs learn speech through singing; if they learn to pronounce words incorrectly, it may take a long time to unlearn.

3. Use Quality Instruments

Rather than buying a "bargain" box filled with instruments that have a bad sound quality as well as being breakable (or even dangerous), choose a few high-quality instruments that your students can share.

4. Use Music with Discretion

Do you hear your refrigerator buzzing? Most of us don't – because we're so used to it, we block it out. If music is an effective tool, use it when you most need it. Playing music all day won't make children smarter – it will just teach them to tune it out.

5. Include by Adapting

A few simple adaptations will help in including children with special needs in regular education music settings. If the class is learning to play the recorder, for example, the music teacher can identify one or two "pedal" tones for each piece: the child with special needs can play just those two notes on a recorder, or on a resonator bell, for example. Children who cannot participate in singing can play rhythm instruments to accompany their peers.

6. Use Live Music

You can sing! Live music is, in most cases, much more effective than recorded music. If you sing the songs, you can change the tempo and volume according to the mood and behaviour of the class, you can pause to allow time for responses or to cue attention, and you can change the words to fit your lesson.

❏ ❏ ❏

Part III
THE INDIAN INFLUENCE

1. The Indian Way of Healing Sounds

Music therapy is a scientific method of effective cures of disease through the power of music. It restores, maintains and improves emotional, physiological and psychological well-being. The articulation, pitch, tone and specific arrangement of *swars* (notes) in a particular *raga* stimulates, alleviates and cures various ailments inducing electro-magnetic change in the body.

Music therapy has a long history dating back to the ancient Orphic school in Greece. Pythagoras, Plato and Aristotle, among others, were well aware of the prophylactic and therapeutic powers of music. Even the Old Testament mentions music therapy where King David is said to have cured an illness by playing on the harp. Hippocrates, the father of modern medicine, used music to cure human diseases. In ancient Egypt music was used to lessen the pain of women during childbirth. Ibn Sina, a famous Arabic writer, has written in detail on this subject.

In India legend has it that Thyagaraja, the famous musician of South India, brought a dead person back to life by singing the composition *Nav Jeevan Dhara* in *Raga Bihari*. In 1729, a physician Richard Browne wrote the famous text *Medicina Musica*, which describes the use of music as medicine. And one Dr Burnell has mentioned a manuscript named *Raga Chikitsa* in the collections of Saraswati Mahal Library in Tanjore, which deals with the various ragas that can be used for curing numerous ailments.

So what exactly is music? "Music is a kind of inarticulate, unfathomable speech which leads us to the edge of the infinite and lets us for a moment gaze in that," observed Carlyle. Music is basically a sound or nada generating particular vibrations, which moves through the medium of ether present in the atmosphere and affects the human body. Sarangdev mentions in his *Sangeet Ratnakar* that *ahata nada* or music is always produced by striking or *aghata* by a living being on an instrument of any kind. So music is a power or universal energy in the form of ragas.

Matanga (9-10th century AD) was the earliest writer to define raga. According to him, "raga is that kind of sound composition consisting of melodic movements, which has the effect of colouring the hearts of men".

"There are four sources of raga: folk songs, poetry, devotional songs of mystics and compositions of classical musicians. While harmony is the characteristic of Western music, Indian music is pure melody. The general term for melody in India is raga or ragini," says M.S. Randhawa in *Kangra Ragmala.*

Symphonies of raga have a definite soothing effect on the mind as well as the body. Repeated listening to the particular raga being chosen for a particular disease produces a network of sound vibration. The muscles, nerves and the chakras of the affected part are contracted when one impulse is given and relaxed during the interval between two impulses.

Thus, during contraction of the tissue, musical notes make the blood flow out from that particular area and in the interval there is relaxation and a state of reduced pressure is produced in these areas. Thus the blood from the adjacent area will flow there. This process is repeated again and again and the blood flow and energy flow in that part is enhanced. This makes quick, fast healing energy from UEF (universal energy field) to HEF (human energy field) transmitted by the strokes of the different tones of raga which affects the CNS (central nervous system) because the roots of the auditory nerves are more widely distributed and have more connections than any other nerves in the body.

Music beats have a very close relationship with heartbeats. Music having 70-75 beats per minute equivalent to the normal heartbeat of 72 has a very soothing effect. Likewise rhythms that are slower than 72 beats per minute create a positive suspense on the mind and body since the mind-body complex anticipates that the music will speed up and this restored vital energy gives a deep relaxation to the body. Rhythms that are faster than the heart rate excite and rejuvenate the body.

Hindustani classical music considers ragas as depicting specific moods. An appropriate mood is to be evoked in the listener's mind before initiating the musical treatment. *Kafi Raga* evokes a humid, cool, soothing and deep mood, while *Raga Pooriya Dhanasri* evokes a sweet, deep, heavy, cloudy and stable state of mind. *Raga Mishra Mand* has a very pleasing, refreshing, light and sweet touch, while *Bageshwari* arouses a feeling of darkness, stability, depth and calmness.

Tansen composed a late-night raga for Akbar.

Music is considered the best tranquilliser in modern times of anxiety, tension and high blood pressure. *Raga Darbari* is considered very effective in easing tension. It is a late-night raga composed by Tansen for Akbar to relieve his tension after a hectic day in court. This raga belongs to *Asawari Thaat* and is a complete raga containing all the seven notes. The seven notes are taken from various natural sounds of birds and animals. Pandit Jasaraj's *Ram Ko Sumiran Kar* in *Vilambil Ek Tal* is one of the best available recordings of this majestic raga. Pandit Raghunath Seth's *Raga Darbari* (instrumental) in a music therapy cassette named *Tanav* is specially composed for easing tension.

Dr Balaji Tambe of Maharashtra has proved through his research that *Raga Bhupali* and *Todi* give tremendous relief to patients of high blood pressure. *Raga Ahir Bhairav* is supposed to sustain the chords, which automatically brings down blood pressure. This raga is a combination of *Kafi* and *Bhairav*. Pandit Jasaraj's *Aaj to Anand Hi Anand* in *Druti-Teen Tal* is one of the best vocal performances of this beautiful raga.

Raga Malkauns and *Raga Asawari* help cure low blood pressure. *Malkauns* is a very prominent raga of *Bhairavi Thaat* (composition of musical notes from which the raga originates) and is one of the oldest ragas of Indian classical music. *Re* and *pa* are absent in this raga; all the other notes used are *komal* (soft). The timeless performance by Pandit Onkarnath Thakur in *Paga ghunghroo baandh Meera nache re* is one of the best-known examples of this raga.

For heart ailments *Raga Chandrakauns* is considered very helpful. Certain other prominent ragas for relaxation and easing tension are *Raga Tilak-kamod, Hansdhwani, Kalavati Durga* etc. They evoke a very pleasing effect on the nerves. For patients suffering from insomnia who need peaceful sonorous sleep, *Raga Bihag* and *Bahar* have a wonderful effect.

Ragas are closely related to different parts of the day according to changes in nature and development of a particular emotion, mood or sentiment in the human mind. *Bhairav* is sung an hour before dawn, *Ramkali* at dawn, *Vilavali* at sunrise, *Sarang* at noon, *Nata* and *Malava* in the afternoons, *Gaudi* in the evenings, *Kalyan* at night, *Kedara, Chandra* and *Bihag* late in the night.

Music therapy treatment is conducted either early morning, evening or night. One should avoid long music sessions on an empty stomach. Music sessions should be of one-hour duration with two or three short sessions with breaks.

❏ ❏ ❏

2. The Perception of Sound

All that exists in the manifest state does so because it has a complementary unmanifest state that is its source, says Elizabeth Haich, elaborating on years of research on the subject. We perceive light, therefore, in the manifested state only because there exists an unmanifested state which is total darkness, she says. We hear sound only because there is an unmanifested state of absolute silence, the state from which all sound originates.

Therefore, sound is the source of silence and silence is the source of sound. All sound dissolves into silence; silence tends to manifest into sound. It is because of this principle of sound and silence that esoteric musical philosophy recognised two complementary components which in Sanskrit writings are referred to as the "struck sound" – which we can hear – and the "unstruck sound" – which we cannot hear.

Unstruck sound is the centre from which all struck sound emanates. Through the practice of music one may experience the state of absolute equilibrium, absolute balance, perfect unity and harmony which exists both at its centre and our own, for both are identical to and inseparable from the unmanifest creative state of the cosmos. At the centre lies the perfect emptiness of total union to which we, music, and all manifested things aspire.

"Things", in essence, are not "things" but processes in a state of continual becoming. Therefore music, as a manifestation of energy, is a force that interacts with the physical world for music influences our thoughts, our emotions, our dense physical bodies and the electro-magnetic field that surrounds us.

Because the entire physical cosmos is in continual movement, writes Lama Govinda with a great degree of affirmation in *Foundations of Tibetan Mysticism*... "All things or beings produce sounds according to their own nature and to the particular state in which they find themselves. This is because these beings and things are aggregates of atoms that dance and by their movements produce sounds. When the rhythm of the dance changes, the sound it produces also changes... Each atom perpetually sings its songs and the sound creates each moment dense and subtle sound forms. Just as there exist creative sounds, there exist destructive sounds. He who is able to produce both can, at will, create or destroy."

These philosophical concepts became the foundation upon which all musical practice of the ancient world was formed. The musicians, shamans, priests, prophets and philosophers held one philosophical concept in common – that music represents a microcosm of the order of the universe and follows cosmological laws, and that through the practice of music one could better understand these laws as well as the intelligence behind them. The ethereal quality of music was regarded as a miniature of the ethereal substance that fills the vast spaces of the cosmos within which the celestial bodies move.

The rhythm of music, for example, reflected the movement of galaxies, stars and planets, of the sun and moon, the cycle of seasons, days and nights, the tides of the seas and the birth and death of our own cells. Music was regarded as the force that could bring about harmony within the mind and body of Man, within the human community and ultimately within the heavenly bodies themselves – the fluidity of energy changing and merging with energy, the primordial force of the cosmos.

❏ ❏ ❏

3. Indian Music Therapy Practitioners

The Indian music therapy scene is fairly underdeveloped when compared to the progress made in the west after decades of serious and creative experimentation. But there are pockets of excellence saving the day for the inheritors of AUM, the first sound ever that led to Creation, according to the Rig Veda. Said Swami Vivekananda: "Brahman first manifested itself as Sound, and then as Form." The Bible also mentions that the cosmos was created through sound: "In the Beginning, there was the Word. And the Word was God."

So whether one refers to it as Aum, the Word, the Big Bang (as scientists would have it), it seems that everything begins with sound and Creation, including music therapy.

The love of music was the pivotal force for Dr Manjula Devi, which made her study medicine and specialise in psychiatry. Now Assistant Professor of psychiatry in National Institute of Mental Health and Neuro Sciences (NIMHANS), she prescribes music therapy for most of her patients. It is essentially an adjunct to mainstream medicare.

With formal training in music from the age of three, Dr Devi went on to complete a diploma in music before embarking on study and a career in conventional medicine. "People with a musical background cope better with stress and tension when compared with those without any footing in music," she says with conviction.

In her private consultation, Dr Devi recommends music therapy to patients. She has also donated cassettes of assorted compositions to the cancer ward at a hospital in Mumbai. "Patients who are insomniacs, mentally challenged and those who are sexually dysfunctional have been successfully treated with music therapy," she says.

But, she insists, that music therapy is not a cure in itself. It has to be associated with psychotherapy and other oral medicines. "Moreover, one shouldn't practise this therapy without assistance from experienced musicians or therapists because one might just end up aggravating the pain or the disorder."

Dr Devi is not alone. She is part of a select band. A neurosurgeon, Dr Lakshmi Narayanan, also prescribes music therapy to patients with mental and neurological disorders and those in a coma. He says, "Music helps the pace of recovery and we use it when the patient is in coma."

Prakash Sontakke, a classical singer and instrumentalist, however feels that, "One should definitely have a grounding in music and should harbour some affinity towards music for the therapy to work." Sontakke has worked with several organisations in implementing music therapy. His father Raja Bhau Sontakke, also a renowned singer, runs a music institute in Bangalore. His guru was the great Omkarnath Thakur, who, during his visit to Rome, it is believed, made a profound impression on Benito Mussolini, curing Il Duce of insomnia.

Bharathamuni in his book, *Natyashastra*, has mentioned 108 karmas, each of them dealing with a human disorder and its cure. The Vedas have also mentioned different ragas to cure many ailments. Legend has it that Sushrutha, the Father of Medicine in India, used music to dull pain during surgery. Experts in the field insist that almost all ragas have a corresponding human organ that works when the ragas are used.

Music is *naada* that generates specific vibrations that move through the medium of the atmosphere and affect the human body. Music can be defined as universal energy assuming the form of ragas, says Raja Bhau Sontakke.

The articulation, pitch, ragas, swaras and their arrangement stimulate and cure certain ailments of the body. When a certain kind of music, preferably classical or soft music, is listened to, the human body reacts to it and repeated listening of that music results in producing a network of sound vibrations that treats a particular ailment. Many say that music by itself is therapy, like dancing, painting and Yoga.

According to Dr Devi, "Music as therapy can work miracles in patients who are mentally challenged. Well, each case has to be dealt with separately and there is no prescribed use of such therapies. We have to conduct research personally and know the patient and then use the music that is conducive to the particular patient." She cites the case of Rajashekar, a patient with Specific Learning Disorder, who couldn't read or write. "But he learnt music just by listening since that was the only thing he could do, and he eventually learnt classical music."

Ragas are closely related to different parts of the day according to changes in nature and development of a particular emotion, mood or sentiment. For those with insomnia, *Raga Bihag* and *Bahar* have a wonderful effect. *Bhairav* is sung an hour before dawn, *Ramkali* at dawn, *Vilavali* at sunrise, *Sarang* at noon, *Nata* and *Malava* in the afternoon, *Gaudi* in the evening, *Kalyan* at night, *Kedara, Chandra* and *Bihag* late in the night.

Our Vedic texts are the source of information on music to be used in healing. One of the oldest recorded manuscripts, *Gandharva Veda*, mentions the use of music in replicating nature's rhythm and harmony. There are many instances where music has been used for healing disorders.

Music therapy can be practised in many ways. For instance, the therapist and the client may compose music, lyrics and songs to express particular feelings. One may learn to play the sitar or the piano to improve fine motor skills, while another may use instruments to improvise unspoken emotions. However, knowing how to play or sing is not a necessary factor to undergo therapy. Simply listening to the music is sufficient. And if you are into a self-help session, you can surely carry that on by listening to music from your collection of favourites.

Vyjayanthi Kasi, a Bangalore-based dancer, has been doing research on dance and music therapy for the past five years and has treated physically- and mentally-challenged patients. She has also dealt with the visually and hearing impaired with the help of dance and music therapy.

"My students have changed remarkably for the better after I started teaching them dance and music," says Vyjayanthi, who conducts free workshops for such students in association with special schools. "It is a challenging task," she says, "to handle mentally-challenged students since each student is different from the other. First, I identify their needs and stimulate and inspire them into a character and then assign them the role they have to portray. Along with that, I play the music that balances their roles in the play. For example, if a child is short-tempered, then he becomes Rama in the show. That is to portray a calm and composed look."

Vyjayanthi also receives cases of girls who are abused and ill-treated by their in-laws. "I give them lessons in dance so that they can channel their thoughts away from their present and release their tensions," she says.

Vyjayanthi also receives e-mails from distressed parents with requests to treat their children for various disorders. Requests can range from increasing the child's appetite to developing concentration and memory power etc. A number of people also approach her art institute for therapy. According to her, music therapy has been used from the beginning of time. "People have been using music as therapy without even realising it."

Then there's Dr Sadanand Sardeshmukh, who has achieved great feats in music therapy and has been practising in India for over three decades. Patients visit his Pune and Mumbai clinics from all over India for his excellent diagnosis.

Ganapathy Sachchidananda Swamiji from Karnataka, who has a following both within and outside the country, conducts spiritual music concerts for meditation and healing (*Nada Chikitsa*) in India and abroad. He prescribes 'melodious medicine' in his music recordings and concerts for many ailments and disorders, be it coma, cancer, migraine or depression. He believes in combining music therapy with Ayurveda, Psychology, Gemology and Astrology. "There is no complication about it, once you are in tune with the modus operandi," he says. "Listen with your heart and not with your intellect. Both the healer-musician and the listener should concentrate." Listening, he says, is a special technique of sense control.

Swamiji has identified 72,000 nerves and 14 important nodes that play a vital part in health problems ranging from palpitations to alcoholism.

Music therapy also has other adherents among renowned singers like M. Balamuralikrishna, Kunnakudi Vaidyanathan and Pandit Ravi Shankar. Kunnakudi Vaidyanathan is the director of the Raga Research Centre in Chennai where the musicians and physiotherapists work together to probe the benefits of music in healing.

In India, music and its benefits have been known to every generation. But there are very few who actually cure disorders and ailments. Here, music is given the status of being sacred and has not yet reached the purist's echelons of academia and research centres.

4. Aum - The Unstruck Sound

ncient teachings and modern science agree on this score: you, I, all living beings and all things in existence are, at their most essential level, made up of vibrating, pulsing energy.

For millennia, mystics have recounted their experience of this energy, which is said to manifest in our hearing awareness as a humming vibration around and within everything else.

In the Sanskrit tradition, this sound is called *Anahata Nada*, the "Unstruck Sound". Literally, this means "the sound that is not made by two things striking together". The point of this particular distinction is that all ordinary audible sounds are made by at least two elements: bow and string; drum and stick; two vocal cords; two lips against the mouthpiece of the trumpet; the double reed of the oboe; waves against the shore; wind against the leaves... All sounds within our range of hearing are created by things visible or invisible, striking each other or vibrating together, creating pulsing waves of air molecules which our ears and brain interpret as sound.

Creation began with Aum or the "Unstruck Sound".

So, sound that is not made of two things striking together is the sound of primal energy, the sound of the cosmos itself. Don Campbell, an authority on the subject and from whom we have borrowed liberally, likens this unstruck vibration to the humming of an electrical transformer, or the (to our ears) unheard hummings of atoms and molecules.

The ancients say that the audible sound that most resembles this unstruck sound is the syllable AUM (or OM). Tradition has it that this ancient mantra is composed of four elements. The first three are vocal sounds: A, U, and M. The fourth sound, unheard, is the silence which begins and ends the audible sound, the silence which surrounds it.

There are several traditional and allegorical interpretations of this ancient sound.

The loveliest explanation of AUM is found within the ancient Vedic and Sanskrit traditions. We can read about AUM in the marvellous *Manduka Upanishad*, which explains the four elements of AUM as an allegory of the four planes of consciousness.

"A" resonates in the centre of the mouth. It represents normal waking consciousness, in which subject and object exist as separate entities. This is the level of mechanics, science, logical reason, the lower three chakras. Matter exists on a gross level, is stable and slow to change.

Then the sound "U" transfers the sense of vibration to the back of the mouth, and shifts the allegory to the level of dream consciousness. Here, object and subject become intertwined in awareness. Both are contained within us. Matter becomes subtle, more fluid, rapidly changing. This is the realm of dreams, divinities, imagination, the inner world.

"M" is the third element, humming with lips gently closed. This sound resonates forward in the mouth and buzzes throughout the head. (Try it.) This sound represents the realm of deep, dreamless sleep. There is neither observing subject nor observed object. All are one, and nothing. Only pure Consciousness exists – unseen, pristine, latent, covered with darkness. This is the cosmic night, the interval between cycles of Creation – the womb of the Divine Mother.

It might be said that the ultimate aim of Yoga is to enter this third dreamless realm while awake. Yoga means "yoke" or "join". Through Yoga we "join" our waking consciousness to its "source" in the world of pure, quality-less Consciousness.

Which brings us to the fourth sound of AUM, the primal "unstruck" sound within the silence at the end of the sacred syllable. In fact, the word "silence" itself can be understood only in reference to "sound". We hear this silence best when listening to sound, any sound at all, without interpreting or judging the sound. Listening fully, openly, without preconceptions or expectations. The sound of music, the sound of the city, the sound of the wind in the forest. All can give us the opportunity to follow the path of sound into the awareness of the sound behind the sound.

When one really "listens" to this silent sound, this unstruck vibration, one comes inevitably to stillness, to pure and open existence. The poet Gerhart Hauptmann says the aim of all poetry is "to let the Word be heard resounding behind words". The sound behind the sound... And, in making the sound of AUM, we hear this unstruck sound most clearly in the instant when the last humming vibrations of the "M" fade away. At that moment, that instant separating audible sound and silence, the veil is thinnest, and our listening awareness is most expansive.

At that moment of silence, to use William Blake's words, the "doors of perception" are cleansed, and "everything would appear to man as it is, infinite".

One excellent exercise with the sacred AUM sound involves a more modern interpretation of its elements. In short: "A" is the sound of infinite expanding energy in the cosmos, the energy of Unity Consciousness and Divine Love; "U" is the sound of that very energy manifesting and materialising in our waking reality; with the sound of "M" we absorb and integrate that energy into our own being. In the silence after the sound, we give thanks and allow the process to resonate within us.

Try this: stand comfortably, with feet shoulder-width apart, hands and arms hanging easily at your sides. Prepare to make the "AUM" sound, all three vowels in one seamless breath. Inhale gently, easily, expanding into your belly as you breathe. Open your mouth fully as you inhale, as if to "inhale" the "A" sound itself, creating the intention of the sound before the sound actually begins.

Then, as you begin to make the "A" sound, raise your arms out to the side, as if opening to embrace the entire cosmos. Then, as your voice transitions seamlessly to the "U" sound, extend your arms to the front, as if to hold something precious and powerful in your hands. You might wish to visualise some shape, round and energetic, manifesting between the palms of your hands. Then, gliding from "U" to the "M" sound, bring your hands, and whatever they may contain, to your heart centre. Finally, in the echo of the silence, bring your palms to your chest, pressing them lovingly to your heart. Breathe gently.

Repeat this exercise several times. It is remarkably centring and relaxing.

The most important aspect of this second form of AUM is the combination of sound and movement. It really doesn't matter what "images" you create in your mind as you do this exercise, or what specific significance you choose to attribute to each of the individual vowel sounds. The mere fact that you are intoning this ancient sound, and combining it with gentle intuitive movements of the upper body, will have a naturally gentle and balancing effect on your body, mind, emotions, and spirit.

In that state, we can best hear the *Anahata Nada*, the unstruck sound behind the sound, the very sound of the Self.

5. Audible Prana: The Power of Vibrating Breath

David Gordon is a singer and vocal coach from California. He is on the voice faculty of the University of California at Berkeley, and Sonoma State University. He is also the Education Director and resident vocal coach of the Carmel Bach Festival. He has spent many long years researching the power of AUM. He shares a few of his experiences with us.

It is evident that AUM, the most powerful sound in the world, has been exported from India for further, more chiselled and concentrated research. Aum has entered every part of the world and is still being studied for its mystery, power and control. Aum travelled with Yoga all over the world to mystify and enchant audiences across cultures.

"My first experience of the power of the voice was during a Yoga session years ago," says Gordon. "We concluded with a silent meditation, and ended the meditation with the usual Om. But this time, the teacher suggested that we prolong the sound, entering more fully into the awareness of the vibrations of the tone. The group began toning, each of us breathing at our own natural pace, so the group sound was continuous. When the sound ended, it seemed like my entire being was still vibrating. This experience opened a new door of perception to me.

"Soon after, another wise teacher invited me to realise the very concept of Om. We focused awareness on the breath, imagining what the tone would sound and feel like even before the sound began. We then initiated the audible tone with a low murmur, dark and breathy: the sound of 'uh' as in the word 'cup'. Through this low, unformed, earthy sound

I experienced more fully the reality that it is my breath itself that vibrates to produce this sound. I deepened my connection with prana. It was as if respiration gave me inspiration.

"Only later I realised that we were practising an aspect of Nada Yoga – the use of self-generated sound vibration to draw awareness inward in order to experience the deeper layers of the self. Ever since those early experiences, I have been fascinated with the connections of breath, sound and spirit. I even found connections in the language itself. Our English word 'spirit' comes from the Latin word *spiritus*, which connotes both 'breath' and 'spirit'. Many other languages use related word forms to denote breath and spirit."

Breathing is a basic human need. We can exist only minutes without breath. And so the arts of Pranayama, chanting, toning, and singing all derive their power from a basic and elemental human function. "I love this connection of sound and spirit: by uniting sound and breath, we release physiological tension in specific areas, induce relaxation, energise and promote deep breathing with prolonged exhalations. We balance the body's subtle energies and powerfully draw our awareness deep within, while expressing ourselves outward through the sounds we generate. This simultaneous inward and outward movement integrates who we are inwardly with how and what we are externally. It develops a willingness to be heard, unlocks creativity, and enhances self-acceptance."

The self-generated sounds of toning are a natural breathing exercise. To make a prolonged sound, you must breathe fully and exhale in a steady, slow stream. Here is a simple exercise:

Stand in Tadasana (feet shoulder-width apart, firmly on the floor; arms at your sides). Inhale, raising the arms high above your head, gently reaching your hands toward the ceiling. Exhaling, lower the arms while toning AH. Find the pitch that feels best. Time the movement so that the tone is complete when the movement is complete. Do this five times, then stand in stillness and take in the effect.

The power of sound is that it makes us mindful of inner, subtler levels of vibration. Tension and relaxation, joy and depression, clarity and confusion have different vibrations. Whatever experience at the physical, mental, or emotional levels is the result of what is occurring at the energy level of vibration.

When you tone, introversion is deepened. At first, the vibration deep within the physical body becomes a focus while toning aloud. When the external sound is extinguished, the vibration continues, and the awareness of this subtle sensation continues to draw the practitioner into meditative stillness. Through respiration we are led to a deeper connection with the spirit.

6. Applying Self-Generated Sound in Yoga

Marcia Goldberg has led workshops and trainings on Yoga, meditation, spiritual attunement and self-discipline throughout North America for more than 20 years. The unique combination of sound and postures that she has developed combines her many years of personal experience and study in the field of Yoga with the science of the power of sound.

Marcia first began studying Yoga with a group that met in a circular room lit by starlight and candles. "One evening, seven of us stayed after class," she says. "We sat in a circle and with each exhalation made a sound, the sound of Om. When we finished, I discovered that an hour had passed, although it seemed to me to have been only five minutes. Through sound, I had entered a world of timelessness, harmony, and peace that has called to me ever since.

"What I didn't know then was that we were practising an aspect of Nada Yoga – the use of self-generated sound vibration to draw our awareness inward in order to experience the deeper layers of the self. In recent years, I have continued to explore the power of sound through toning (the practice of sounding elongated vowels) and began integrating sound with my formal practice of postures."

According to Marcia, joining toning with the practice of Yoga has many benefits. At the physiological level, toning releases tension in specific areas, induces relaxation, energises, and promotes deep breathing with prolonged exhalations. Energetically, it balances the body's subtle energies and powerfully draws the awareness deep within.

When we tone out loud, we increase our level of introversion and, at the same time, offer ourselves outward through the sounds we generate. This capacity to move inward and outward simultaneously promotes integration of who we are with how we are externally.

Toning develops willingness to be heard, empowerment in bringing forth who we are into the outside world, and self-acceptance. Groups that tone together find there is a natural bonding that occurs as their individual sounds join together in a group experience.

Toning is easy to learn. "I use seven vowel sounds, each one corresponding to a chakra," says Marcia. "Working up the chakras, the sounds are uh (as in up), oo (as in who), oh (as in boat), ah (as in far), eh (as in get), ee (as in free), mm (a hum with the mouth closed). Each sound is vocalised on a long exhalation at whatever pitch (high or low) is comfortable."

Toning can be combined with Yoga in many ways. Sound linked with movement can be included in warm-ups to energise and oxygenate the body; to integrate breath, mind, and body; to connect to *hara* (core spinal energy); and to relax a group into receiving themselves and each other. Toning can be used as a seated meditation practice or a meditation-in-motion practice, and is of great benefit to special groups of Yoga students who may find movement difficult.

Try this experiment to explore how self-generated sound releases unnecessary tension:

Sit in the Hero Pose (Virasana). Bend the left arm and place the left hand on the spine, palm out. Keep the left shoulder down and back. Stretch the fingers up. Extend the right arm straight up along the ear. Maintain the right arms stretch as you bend it at the elbow and grasp the left hand with the right. Notice the sensations in the shoulders and your arms. Release the posture

From a seated position, with arms relaxed, begin to tone the sound ah. This is done as an elongated sound in the same way that you would chant a continuous Om. Tone at a pitch where you feel the vibration. As you tone ah, notice the vibrations in your body from the sound. Search for the vibrations in and around the area that was most tight when you performed the posture. Then become silent and continue to send the sound ah to that same area. When you feel ready, perform the posture again and note again your comfortable range of movement.

During holding of a posture, when you tone towards the end of holding, introversion is deepened. The vibration deep within the physical body becomes a focus while toning aloud. When the external sound is extinguished, the vibration continues, and the awareness of this subtle sensation continues to draw the practitioner into the meditative stillness of the asana supporting the flow into spontaneous movement.

Toning is an excellent practice for seated meditation as well. In this practice one vowel is sounded for 10-20 minutes. This is followed by silence with a focus on listening internally. Particularly effective when done in a group, toning leads some practitioners to awareness of deep internal places.

The power of sound is that it directly affects vibration. Everything is vibration. As you sit and read this you are vibrating at physical and subtle levels, as well as experiencing the vibration of the cosmos. Tension and relaxation, joy and depression, clarity and confusion have different vibrations. What we experience at the physical, mental, or emotional levels is the result of what is occurring at the energy level of vibration. The practice of Yoga can be described as the science of vibration.

❏ ❏ ❏

7. Nada Yoga –
The Yoga of Sound

Nada Yoga means "union through sound". It is the ancient spiritual art and science of inner transformation through sound and tone. Meditation on sound is one universal path to Self-Realisation, accessible to anyone, and appropriate for people of any religion or spiritual aspiration.

The term "Yoga" means to combine, coordinate, harmonise, integrate. Actually, there are many varieties of Yoga, generally grouped into five categories:

- Jnana Yoga, the Yoga of knowledge and self-inquiry;
- Bhakti Yoga, the Yoga of devotion;
- Karma Yoga, the Yoga of service;
- Kriya Yoga, the Yoga of technique;
- Raja Yoga, a Yoga integrating all the other four forms;
- Hatha Yoga, a basic form of Kriya Yoga, is the Yoga of physicality, postures, and movement. It's probably the most well-known form of Yoga. However, the main classical text on Yoga – the *Yoga Sutras* of Patanjali – discusses physical postures (Hatha Yoga) in only three of its two hundred verses.

Within the heading of Kriya Yoga, or Yoga of technique, there are several subtly different forms of Yoga, which teach meditation on sound as a path to spiritual growth and awareness. The three principal forms of this variety of Yoga are Nada, Laya, and Surat Shabda Yoga. The subtle differences between these three are many and beyond the scope of mere explanation.

❏ ❏ ❏

8. Absorption in Sound

Our mind easily becomes absorbed in sound. This is why everybody – even infants and animals – enjoys listening to music. When the mind is fully concentrated on anything, there arises a feeling of inner bliss. In Nada Yoga, we learn that the source of the sound may be external or internal. The sound may be "gross" or "subtle". That is, it may be "struck" out loud (Sanskrit: *ahat*), as from a voice or musical instrument; or "unstruck" and outwardly silent (Sanskrit: *anahat*), arising inwardly as from the subtle currents of energy or prana moving throughout the body.

With practice, concentration on carefully selected outer or "struck" sounds will enable the mind to become calm and transparent. At this point you may begin to become aware of the subtle inner "unstruck" sounds. You might perceive inner sounds that seem like bells, or flutes, or even a hum like an electrical transformer. Some of these sounds are actually just the sounds of your own body: blood pumping, or the electrical energy of nerves and inner ear. Other, deeper sounds are the "sounds behind the audible sound". It is into this deeper realm that Nada Yoga can take you.

Some traditions tell us that this subtle, inner sound originates in the "heart chakra of the subtle body", considered the centre of unstruck sound. Yogic tradition connects this inner sound with Kundalini itself.

In Nada Yoga, you concentrate on these finer and deeper sounds, moving from the outer to the inner realm, moving awareness from outer to inner sounds (Sanskrit: *nadam*), while all the time gently easing your mind into relaxed concentration and focus. This is a highly enjoyable form of meditation and relatively effortless: as you meditate, your entire being, every cell and atom and part of you, is being purified and balanced by the sounds that you are focusing on.

Remember, whatever you pay attention to, you become. "Where you put your treasure, there you shall also find your heart." Therefore, it is very important that you choose positive and enlightening music and sounds for this meditation.

How to Begin

According to David Gordon, who has researched Yoga and sound for the better part of his working life, one easy way to begin practice of Nada Yoga is to start with beautiful music. You must choose music which sustains a level mood: calming, quiet, maintaining an even loudness and emotion. Music of different types can be used: "New Age" music; Eastern music, the North Indian sitar; Japanese shakuhachi; or Native American flute music, which are all good choices. Choose Western classical music with care; often the dynamic and emotional range is too great for this meditative use. Whatever you choose, it must be instrumental music – no voices. Voices and words are too "specific" and distracting.

At first, simply sit quietly and focus all your attention on the music for 10-15 minutes once or twice a day. Continue this practice with regularity, listening to the same type of music, always with your fullest concentration. Gradually you may be able to hear subtle sounds that come from within, rather than the audible sounds from outside. As you begin to be aware of the inner sounds, listen to them and focus on them. Then you can gradually change your meditation from listening to music to listening to the subtle sounds.

Go at your own speed with this. Each experience is unique. Awareness of inner sound may happen sooner – or later – but it will happen. Finally, you will no longer need music for meditation at all, and may use it or not, as you wish. Then continue listening to the inner sounds for your meditation practice everyday. Your perception of the sounds may change as your body and mind become purified and elevated. Just continue to focus on the inner sound or "nadam" daily.

This form of Nada Yoga is actually much easier than it sounds. The wonderful bonus of this practice – meditating with music – is that the process, the journey itself, is highly pleasant. Every step of the way you are bathing yourself in uplifting sounds and music, balancing and healing your heart, mind and spirit. Thus, no matter what the specific "meditative" outcome, you can receive only benefits from this pursuit. Your listening skills will also improve, and you will become more sensitive not only to music and sound, but to the subtle emotions and energies within yourself and in others. You will "listen" to others more completely and directly, and you'll find you are able to hear what others are really saying, no matter how loudly they speak...

❑ ❑ ❑

9. Toning

Toning is the creation of extended vocal sounds on a single vowel in order to experience the sound and its effects in other parts of the body. No melody, no words, no rhythm, and no harmony – just the sound of the vibrating breath. It's a simple, yet powerful, technique, accessible to everyone regardless of vocal ability or training. Through toning, you can immediately experience the effects of sound on your physical, mental, emotional, and spiritual well-being.

By literally massaging body and mind from the inside out, meditative toning can help you focus and relax; release negative emotions; reduce stress; and improve stamina and concentration.

Toning synchronises the brainwaves and helps relieve tension within a few minutes. Toning is also a wonderful technique for developing your voice-ear connection and enhancing your power of listening to everything around you.

Most of all, toning restores balance and harmony to the mind and body. It can help you awaken and deepen your sense of self, and align you to the deepest vibrations of soul and spirit. On the path of toning, you move towards the source of your own inner balance, creativity, well-being, and freedom.

Since the early 1980s, thousands of people have discovered toning, and found it useful for their own health and mental clarity. Doctors, nurses, psychologists, therapists, body workers, teachers, and business professionals have affirmed the benefits of toning in their lives and work.

The power of toning lies in the vowels (like "a-e-i-o-u"). They are much more important to toning than the "pitch" (high or low). The vowels are also intimately related to the body's major energy centres.

These energy centres are called *chakras.* The sacred teachings of both East and West describe them, and correlate them with specific thought patterns and archetypal effects. As we investigate and explore the relationship of the vowels and the chakras, we enrich our understanding of the broad spectrum of energies and emotions within ourselves. Toning connects us with our own inner vibrations.

Try this for starters: Let your intuition choose a vowel for you. Spend several minutes toning it. Begin in the comfortable middle of your vocal range. Then try a lower pitch, then higher, always with moderate volume and without straining. If the vowel feels physically or vocally "wrong" right now, leave it and choose another. Be open to inner experience and sensation, without seeking a specific "result". Explore the sensations of each of these vowels and their total effect on you.

Vowels and Energy

There are many vowel sounds in the human language. For toning we begin by focussing on several principal sounds. Remember, this is not a list of universal truths, just some traditional suggestions.

Possible Vowel Attributes or Related Perceptions:

UU ("who") grounding, calming, relaxing, awareness of physicality, gives sensation of depth, base of spine;

OH ("go") conscious self-image, identity issues, self-confidence, individuality, solar plexus;

AH ("car") centring, expanding, pleasant heartfelt emotions, gives sensation of breadth, heart area;

EY ("pray") self-expression, communication, listening, throat and neck;

EE ("knee") energising, awakening, mental and physical stamina, gives sensation of length, head;

MM (humming, lips closed) balancing, harmonising and integrating, the subtlest and most powerful sounds.

Examples of vowel combinations for balancing and centring (to be vocalised as one continuous full-breath tone exhalation):

UU-AH-EE-MM: Balance and energise. Morning wake-up.

MM-EE-AH-UU: Balance and relax. Before bedtime.

This is a list of just a few traditional suggestions. Your own awareness and experience may be quite different. These are just starting points. There is no "normal" toning experience, only "your" experience! With practice, your inner wisdom will guide you and tell you what vowels you need.

Toning engages your entire being, not just your voice. Whatever specific vowel you may be toning, open your awareness to all physical or energetic sensations, without judgement or analysis. Listen to the vibrations with your whole body, and don't just "hear" with your ears. For example, place the palms of your hands at various places on your body as you tone and allow your hands to feel the sound vibrations.

Enhance your toning with different postures and movements. Whole body involvement deepens and enriches the toning experience. Explore different positions and movements while toning, such as:

◆ Sit on the floor or in a chair;

◆ With your spine expanded vertically stand, either motionless or using intuitive movements of any kind (expansive arm motions are particularly balancing);

◆ Lie quietly on your back with your hands at your sides, experiment with eyes closed or open, focussed or gazing softly;

◆ Tone while walking, working, driving, doing everyday tasks;

◆ Make intuitive, expressive tones while doing Yoga or Tai Chi, express the tone in movement and express the movement in tone.

Let your inner self respond, free from outer expectations. While toning, pay attention to yourself and be open to everything the vibrations may be awakening in you. What is the effect of the tone? Is it soothing? Agitating? Balancing? Focus on the here and now. Open your awareness, and let your intuition guide you to insight.

It is very natural to experience physical sensations or emotions while toning, and it may not always be pleasant. At times you may feel boredom, anger, or any other emotion, positive or negative. Similar experiences are also well known in meditation, Yoga, or any contemplative activity! Know that these feelings are natural, and that they will pass. Don't analyse the feelings or judge yourself for having them. Persevere with open heart and mind, and you will begin to see results, sometimes subtle and sometimes surprising and amazing!

Honour your uniqueness. You are a very complex and utterly unique bio-chemical, electro-magnetic, and spiritual being. No two people experience toning in exactly the same way. Honour and trust your own experience. Experiment, and seek tones which work for you. Allow your voice and tone to bring you into the present moment, and towards self-awareness!

The physical guidelines for toning are very simple:

- Do not tone for more than 20 minutes at any one time.

- A little bit goes a long way. It's often more beneficial to tone more frequently for shorter periods.

- Relax, especially the tongue and jaw.

- Maintain a comfortable and moderate loudness, don't force your voice.

- Be always mindful of healthy posture and deep, full breathing.

- Yawn, stretch, swallow, and move occasionally to release mouth and neck tension.

- Have water and some tissue handy; the energy and physical activity of toning can make your throat dry, or produce excess saliva and mucous. This is harmless.

- If you feel tension or discomfort in your mouth or throat, stop for a few moments, breathe, stretch, yawn, and resume. Sip water.

- Do not force your voice. Stop whenever you need to. You do not have to endure physical or vocal strain.

Remember...

Remember that learning any art takes time, patience, and regular practice. It's more beneficial to tone daily, even for a few minutes, than to tone only infrequently for longer periods. With regular daily practice your body and mind will quickly learn to respond to the tone and vibrations.

Toning is not "singing" and there's no aesthetic judgement involved. The sound you make does not have to be pretty; the point of toning is not the quality of the sound but your experience of the vibration and its results. Listen with your whole being, and be open to the total effect of the sound. Link your voice, breath, and awareness together to enhance your appreciation of your own true power in life.

Remember, there's no "right" way or "wrong" way to tone – only your way! Your natural wisdom and intuition will guide you. Your sound is unique, and the experience is uniquely yours!

10. The Healing Aspects of Toning

The voice has a tremendous ability to be an instrument for healing. Pythagoras recognised the considerable therapeutic power of human speech. He treated diseases through the reading of poetry. He taught his students how a skilful, well-modulated voice, with beautiful words and pleasing meter, could restore balance to the body and soul.

The belief in the healing capacity of the human voice is common to many parts of the world. Shamans and holy men of primitive societies would use a spirit language to commune with higher intelligences so as to extract proper remedies.

Confession has been used by many societies and religions as a means of accelerating the healing process. This process aligns itself with many of modern psychology's psychosomatic remedies. It was used voluntarily by the Apache Indians during times of illness. According to Ted Andrews, an expert on toning for health, the Apaches recognised that all levels of consciousness and action were intimately connected to the physical. By confessing, the individual faced what had created the illness.

More commonly, the Catholic Church still utilises confession. However, it has lost the physical healing aspects that once were associated with it. Today it is more focused upon the spiritual and emotional cleansing, and few now acknowledge its intimacy with physical well-being.

Our speech comprises two elements: consonants and vowels. Every letter and combination of letters has significance. The vowel sounds are the most dynamic aspect of spoken sound, for without them the consonants could not be sounded. Many of the early alphabets excluded the vowels, in the belief that they were too stimulating, causing certain energies to be activated.

The Chaldean alphabet, one of the forerunners of our alphabet, was designed to be a tool for attaining higher wisdom. Their letters, sounds, glyphic forms, and their numerological correspondences provide clues to the more archetypal energies operating and activated through the words.

Mantra Yoga is a technique for human self-realisation through the use of inner sounds or nadas that are awakened through outer toning and chanting. In Tibetan beliefs, the most important musical instrument is the human voice, and the Tibetan shamans are trained in the use of outer sound projection to create inner, esoteric vibrations. They learn to use the head and chest as resonance chambers for the entire human body. The repeated toning of vowels creates a reverberation so that when the chanting stops, the sounds continue to echo within the mind and within the chambers of the body.

Each vowel opens a particular part of the body. This part of the body should be visualised during the inhalation and also when the vowel is spoken or toned internally. This inner sounding is the key to many metaphysical teachings concerning sound and mantras.

Without the inner sounding occurring before the outer, audible sounding, the effects are minimised. The process of Directed Esoteric Toning involves both aspects. It is

Chanting uplifts the spirits.

simple: as we inhale, we focus our minds on the region of the body associated with the vowel, and we sound it silently. Then as we exhale, we vibrate or tone the sound again audibly.

This method of opening by the vowels can be better understood if we realise that breath penetrates deeply into the region concerned, according to our thoughts. The breath takes the energy of prana and combines it with the vowel tones and together they open specific inner regions of the body or consciousness.

Healing Vowel Sounds

U can be used for the pelvis, hips, legs, feet, and lower body in general, O for the lower trunk and abdomen area from the solar plexus to the groin. A is for the chest cavity, heart, and the body as a whole. E is for the throat, upper chest, and head regions. I is for the back, skull and head regions.

If, with the aid of our thoughts and imagination, we can suffuse our whole body with the vowel sounds, we can restore balance and life to all aspects of it. We can use the vowel sounds as an alternative to music in balancing and stimulating the chakras.

Many people excuse themselves from the process of healing through sound, music, or voice by saying they can't play a musical instrument, they can't sing, they can't get to the library to borrow music in the appropriate key, they don't know nursery songs which every child knows and so on. These are mere excuses. If they can speak, they can balance themselves. They don't have to be expert musicians.

Breath is important to the process of toning. Breath refers to that quick intake or gasp of energy that carries an image or thought to the subconscious. All aspects of toning are related to breath. Breath is life. When we become aware of our breathing patterns, we have greater control over them. As we work with toning and become more balanced, our breathing becomes more fluid, healthy, and harmonious.

How to Tone

The purpose of toning is to restore the vibrational pattern of the body (physical and subtle) to its perfect electro-magnetic field so that our spiritual essence can manifest more fully in our physical environment. Voice belongs to the physical body, but it is the instrument of the spiritual self. Being more than body, we need to learn to use it as a tool for higher consciousness and greater health.

Experiment with the toning process. Take the primary vowel sound from your name. Close your eyes and tone the sound slowly. Allow it to find its own volume and length of sound. Initially, don't try and hold it to a particular pitch. Repeat for five to ten minutes. Within this time, it will find its own natural pitch.

After a week of this, you will naturally tone the most harmonious pitch. This is effective in helping develop greater resonance within your own voice. Toning this sound ten to twelve times is balancing to the body and calming to the mind.

Work with all of the vowel sounds. Start with the base chakra and tone each sound five to ten times, moving up through each chakra centre. Use a pitch pipe and experiment with different pitches for the different vowel sounds. Pay attention to areas in which you have difficulty with the tone or at those points where the voice breaks, cracks or fluctuates.

The toning process can be used to heal yourself and to increase self-awareness. As with all healing, relaxation is critical, but the unique aspect of sacred sound is that relaxation occurs as a natural part of the process. You cannot use healing sounds without relieving stress.

❑ ❑ ❑

11. Music, the Foetus and Vedic Chanting

There is enormous research globally on the effect of structured sound on the unborn child. It has been proved that the foetus responds to sound from the 24th week of pregnancy. While sounds are greatly altered as they pass from the outside world to the ear of the foetus, there is more than sufficient stimulation to be heard in the womb. There are documented changes in the heart rate and breathing patterns of the foetus in response to sound stimulation. It has been proved that there is a 'biology in music' and that structured specific sounds heard by the foetus in the womb provide a strong foundation for later learning and behaviour.

Says Giselle Whitwell, a prenatal music therapist, "We now know that the foetus is having first language lessons in the womb. The inflections of the mother tongue are conveyed through speech and song. The singing voice has a richer frequency range than speech. Babies born of deaf mothers miss these important first lessons in language development."

Even in nature, the effects of music are passed on to the offspring in the foetal stage. Dr Alfred Tomatis of France mentions being intrigued by the fact that songbirds hatched by silent foster mothers can't sing. This finding has been replicated by other naturalists too.

In India, Vedic chanting provides a culturally appropriate sound for both the mother and the child. The inherent resonance and rhythms in the chanting will stimulate the child and provide a strong basis for later learning patterns. Listening to Vedic chanting is the first step in early parenting for the couple. It affords an opportunity to be in harmony with the new life growing inside the womb. The pressures of pregnancy are calmed somewhat by Vedic chanting.

While listening to the chants, it is not necessary to understand the meaning of the mantras. The perennial sound vibrations, which exist in the cosmos, connect every cell. Sounds can be understood and related to at three levels:

- *Shabda Anusandhaanam* (perceiving the vibration of sound): When we hear certain sounds, we relate only to the sound vibration that leaves an impact on our system.

- *Artha Anusandhaanam* (perceiving the meaning of sound): The mind will make an effort to comprehend the meaning of the sound, and then relate to the sound.

- *Bhaava Anusandhaanam* (perceiving the emotions/ feelings of sounds): Every sound, whether it has a specific meaning or not, contains a *bhaava* or emotion in it. A sensitive person can hear and feel the intention of the sound.

By listening to Vedic chanting in the prenatal period, it is possible to nourish the child through music into becoming well integrated in his/her physical, emotional, intellectual and spiritual self.

The Ojas Foundation in Chennai is a global Vedic health movement. It promotes the Vedic path to healthy living. Mining the essence of the Vedas, this movement advocates the use of chanting, guided meditation, stress reduction, diet modifications and exercises to deal with health challenges on an everyday basis. The founder, Sri Tartwamasi Dixit, is a Vedic scholar who has extracted specific mantras for specific health problems. The co-founder, Dr Gita Arjun, an obstetrician and gynaecologist from Chennai, uses and helps channel the Vedic knowledge to access the wellspring of healing energies dormant in all of us.

Recently, the Ojas Foundation released *Ojas for the Expectant Mother*, a CD which contains specific mantras culled from the Vedas which impact the child in a positive way.

❑ ❑ ❑

12. Music in Auroville – The City of Dawn

Auroville is an international township, a few kilometres from Pondicherry in the south of India. Warmed throughout the year by an unrelenting Tamilian sun, it is, to paraphrase its charter, a seat of never-ending education and a laboratory of continuous experimentation and growth at all levels in preparation of the 'neo-man'. "It belongs to nobody in particular but to humanity as a whole," adds the charter. In a place of such spiritual significance, music is a core happening. Its agenda is superhuman: to create the man of the super-mind. If music is a tool in this mammoth soul-constructing exercise, it must, quite naturally, have ennobling credentials.

Auroville is not a profit centre in pecuniary terms: it is supported by the United Nations, philanthropists and by the sale of its products. Nobody goes to Auroville, like they do to Mumbai or New York, to rough up the pavements made of gold and get a smattering of gold dust. The agenda of Auroville is as pure as can be. It is the City of Dawn calling people from all over the world to create a self-sustaining agenda for the human race. Despite the heat and the hardship, the Mother's call is clear, "Let your highest aspiration organise your life." Music here, in all its dimensions, is an integral part of the curriculum of the call.

Auroville is over three decades old now. What was once bare, red earth in the dry, arid wilderness of Tamil Nadu and the cradle of the Mother's dream, it is now home to over 50,000 varieties of plants, boasts a green belt, hosts a variety of exotic flora and fauna, houses the Matri Mandir, touted as the next Wonder of the World, and is a lung of beauty, joy, hope, life, oxygen and many new dreams.

Stefano, one of Auroville's musicians, gives his impressions on the music dimension of the township. "If architecture is frozen music, then music is architecture in movement. I see a city of sound that keeps transforming itself. A city in which we live and which we keep building, everyday anew," Stefano says.

Stefano stays in Aurodam, one of the settlements, and does vowel chanting. He gives occasional classes to guests, but "that's it".

For many Auroville musicians, the practice of their instrument has become a way of finding themselves after a full day's work. It has become a sort of active meditation, a way to get in touch with their inner levels, their emotions and creativity. That's probably one of the reasons why there are so many musicians in Auroville, and such a wide spectrum of musical expression.

I have lived in Auroville many times during its life and been privy to the unique relationship Auroville has to music. There are a million sounds everywhere emerging simultaneously: from the trees, from under the carpet, from the sea, from the villagers, from the birds and animals everywhere, from the hissing of rattlesnakes to the cry of the koel, and even from the most sophisticated music systems from around the world. The collection of music is as immense as it is eclectic, as music is used like an auspicious beckoning, applause or conclusion for almost every occasion, however mundane or elevating it may be.

"I use the Hare Krsna music," says Prabhadevipuri, an Italian who lives in Quiet, a settlement on the fringes of Auroville. "I use it heal myself with the right foods and the right vibrations. It has helped." Prabhadevi was recommended surgery for a health problem many years ago but as a Reiki master and yoga instructor, she understood the significance of holistic healing. "I used the right chants, the right foods and listened to the body and I was cured," she says. "Of course, music is miraculous and a healing tool."

"Music in Auroville starts – and here all of Auroville's musicians agree – with the sound of birds," Stefano continues. "Music in Auroville is also the blasting sound from the surrounding villages that at times wakes us up at 4 o'clock in the morning, sometimes lasting all day long, regardless of decibel limits. But that very same blasting 'music' is sometimes very graceful too and, on occasion, intense. I remember one early morning when the sound of birds was merging with some distant Muslim chanting, and it felt as if there was gold in the air."

There are live concerts performed in the township all year long. Quite regularly, there are concerts and recitals of western classical music. These are either played by Aurovilians, by invited artists, or artists just passing by. Indian classical music is more frequently performed, in all its diversity: Carnatic, Hindustani, Dhrupad, Baul, sometimes given by internationally known musicians.

There is also a Sunday night Jazz Café which provides a space for people to meet and for musicians to play and improvise. Actors occasionally join in and sketches emerge out of sheer inventiveness and joy.

As Auroville counts many individuals of different nationalities, backgrounds and depth, it is interesting to note that the general tendency is to play original compositions. Hence a vast display of previously unheard music is one of the main characteristics of Auroville.

From acoustic to amplified, a rich variety of music has been made and performed within the community. Such performances have included intimate chamber music recitals, concerts for choir and orchestra, classical singing, jazz and bossa nova concerts, rock shows for dancing audiences, informal jazz café evenings and private healing sessions.

Auroville's attraction to the offbeat, itinerant musician is best exemplified by Nadaka. Born in Quebec, Canada, Nadaka discovered Sri Aurobindo at 16 and trekked through Afghanistan and Pakistan to reach Amritsar and then Pondicherry.

As everyone knows, the early years in Auroville were tough. "There was no electricity, no tape recorder, only live village music. I changed my original name to Nadaka just like that. Only seven years later did I realise its meaning. It is the sound of OM. It means the one who carries sound," he reveals.

Nadaka met with many well-known musicians but the greatest influence was from Nemat Daman, a Sufi musician from Iran. "He taught me that music was about silence. He would play for eight hours in silence and magic would happen from the space around him. I was beginning to feel the necessity to go into the source of sound." Music had the influence of healing and Nadaka had found it. Like so many others who come to Auroville.

We have long known of the power of sound and music to affect our emotions and moods and ultimately our physical bodies. Tribal music, ceremonial music, devotional music and spiritual chanting are a few well-known examples of how sound can be used to create change. Intense use of ritual chanting can create altered states so powerful that people are known to become impervious to pain during such periods. Prisoners of war have endured incredible situations such as starvation, isolation and physical punishment by humming and singing whenever possible to maintain their sense of self and ultimately keep themselves alive.

Sound has long been used as a communication tool since the beginning of time. Native Americans sent messages by drumbeats. They developed ritual songs and dances for rain, war, hunting, good harvest, marriages and so on.

"Can music help reconfigure the brain?" asks Stefano. "It may be strange to think of rappers and rockers as masters of modern therapy – but current research indicates that time spent listening to music is often time well spent. Music and sound have great potential."

❏ ❏ ❏

13. Plants and Music Treatment

Although ancient seers and Vedic scholars understood the import of sound and music and its connection with healing and well-being, in contemporary India music therapy is used without being accorded overt recognition. For instance, as a child when Pandit Hariprasad Chaurasia suffered from asthma, he was advised by the doctor to take

Pandit Hariprasad Chaurasia was advised to play the flute as he suffered from asthma.

up the flute as an antidotal exercise – something reco-mmended by doctors even today. People who heard him in his twenties recall that his 'phook' or blow was as pure in tonality as it was when he later became famous. Yet, how many doctors would recognise or recommend this as a means of cure for asthmatics?

It's not only human well-being where music has a positive role to play. A report published in Delhi's *Hindustan Times* of August 8, 2002 is a pointer in this direction. Headlined: *Sound of Music Enhances Crop Yield,* the report by Ashok Das mentions how farmers in Krishna district of Andhra Pradesh have been putting music to good use – for reaping a rich harvest!

It seems sugarcane yields in Vuyyur and Laxmipuram areas have shot up by six to eight tonnes per acre after the plants were exposed to music regularly. Crops in neighbouring fields not exposed to music are yielding an average of 33 tonnes. But crops that are being given the acoustic treatment have been reaping a bounty of 38-42 tonnes per acre! Incidentally, these yields are record ones for the state. The extra yield means these farmers earn an extra income of Rs 5,400 to Rs 7,200 (@ Rs 900 per tonne).

The report adds that even the day-to-day growth of plants has shown a substantial increase. These findings have been confirmed by a team of agronomists from IIT, Chennai, who studied crop growth in the fields treated with music and those not treated and found that the former had double the growth rate. These findings were thereafter ratified by a National Remote Sensing Agency satellite data, which showed that cell elongation and multiplication leading to increase in bio-mass was more in the treated plants.

Where Indian farmers are concerned, this should be nothing short of sweet music to their ears, be they sugarcane farmers or others. The Andhra farmers use a simple modus operandi to achieve their record yields. A tape recorder is hoisted on a bamboo pole above the crops and music is played twice a day for half-an-hour each time. Although plants respond to all kinds of music – classical, Western or Indipop! – the

Jagadish Chandra Bose proved that plants respond to musical stimuli.

Andhra plants are said to grow best with a staccato kind of instrumental music that, incidentally, sounds very irritating to human ears! The results of this acoustic treatment vary from plant to plant depending on the music and its frequency.

The venture into music treatment for plants began in 1997-98 when the local KCP Sugar Industries decided to revive the experiments begun by its former chairman B. Maruthi Rao. Using principles of the Bose Theory, pioneered by scientist Jagadish Chandra Bose, Maruthi Rao conducted experiments with crops and proved that plant health and yield could be increased simply by playing them music regularly!

His experiments indicated that a staccato sort of music promotes maximum growth in sugarcane. Thereafter, the company began distributing cassette players and music cassettes to farmers and the encouraging results motivated an increasing number of farmers to adopt music treatment for plants.

❏ ❏ ❏

Part IV
QUERIES & CASE STUDIES

1. Some Important Questions

What *really* is Music Therapy?

Music therapy is an allied health profession in which music is used within a therapeutic relationship to address physical, psychological, cognitive, and social needs of individuals. After assessing the strengths and needs of each client, the qualified music therapist provides the indicated treatment including creating, singing, moving to, and/or listening to music. Through musical involvement in the therapeutic context, the client's abilities are strengthened and transferred to other areas of his or her life.

Music therapy also provides avenues for communication that can be helpful to those who find it difficult to express themselves in words. Research in the music therapy profession supports the effectiveness of music therapy in many areas such as facilitating movement and overall physical rehabilitation, motivating people to cope with treatment, providing emotional support for clients and their families, and providing an outlet for the expression of feelings.

When is Music Therapy prescribed?

Music therapy is the prescribed use of music and musical interventions in order to restore, maintain, and improve emotional, physical, physiological, and spiritual health and well-being. Within this definition are the key elements that define interventions as music therapy.

Abroad, music therapy is essentially prescribed by members of the client's treatment team, which can include doctors, social workers, psychologists, teachers, case workers or parents.

Music is the primary therapeutic tool. Using music to establish a trusting relationship, the music therapist then works to improve the client's physical and mental functioning through carefully structured activities. Examples can include singing, listening, playing instruments, composition, moving to music, and music and imagery exercises.

Music is administered by a trained music therapist. A music therapist's education and training is extensive. Musical interventions are developed and used by the therapist based on his/her knowledge of the music's effect on behaviour, the client's strengths and weaknesses, and the therapeutic goals.

Music therapy works towards specific therapeutic goals and objectives. Goal areas include communicative, academic, motor, emotional, and social skills. It is important to be aware that while clients may develop their musical skills during treatment, these skills are not the primary concern of the therapist. Rather it is the effect such musical development might have on the client's physical, psychological and socio-economical functioning.

What are the kinds of goals a Music Therapist might address?

Music therapists address a number of non-musical goals including improving communication skills, decreasing inappropriate behaviour, improving academic and motor skills, increasing attention span, strengthening social and leisure skills, pain management and stress reduction.

Music therapy can also help individuals on their journey of self-growth and understanding.

What are the typical Music Therapy interventions that might be used in a session?

There is an extensive array of music activities and interventions. For example, the therapist and client might compose songs to express feelings; one client might learn to play the piano to improve fine motor skills, while another client might use instruments to improvise unspoken emotions. Music therapists may also use music and movement activities, singing, lyric discussion or music and imagery to help the client reach their goals.

What are the main therapeutic characteristics of music?

The important therapeutic characteristics are:

♦ Music captivates and maintains attention – it stimulates and utilises many parts of the brain;

♦ Music is easily adapted to, and can be reflective of, a person's abilities;

♦ Music structures time in a way that even the mentally-challenged can understand ("that's the last verse – my exercise session is almost over!");

♦ Music provides a meaningful, enjoyable context for repetition;

♦ Music provides a social context – it sets up a safe, structured setting for verbal and non-verbal communication;

♦ Music is an effective memory aid;

♦ Music supports and encourages movement;

♦ Music taps into memories and emotions;

♦ Music – and the silences within it – provide non-verbal, immediate feedback;

♦ Music is success-oriented – people of all ability levels can participate.

Who can benefit from Music Therapy?

Music therapy benefits everybody irrespective of age, gender, profession or any particular proclivity. You just have to be human to love, enjoy and be moved by music. For that matter, even animals and plants are known to be touched by music.

Music therapy can be especially effective for children with learning difficulties.

Children, adolescents, adults, and the elderly with mental health needs, developmental and learning

121

disabilities, Alzheimer's disease and other ageing-related conditions, those with substance-abuse problems, brain injuries, physical disabilities, and acute and chronic pain, including mothers in labour can all benefit. The list of those who can use it is endless and quite comprehensive.

Where do Music Therapists work?

In the West, music therapists work in psychiatric hospitals, rehabilitative facilities, medical hospitals, outpatient clinics, day-care treatment centres, agencies serving developmentally disabled persons, community mental health centres, drug and alcohol programmes, senior centres, nursing homes, hospice programmes, correctional facilities, halfway houses, schools, and private practice.

As one can see quite clearly, they are required everywhere. However, they are not conventional healing tools and are, at best, adjuncts. Music helps pamper the right environment and that is good enough.

What is the history of Music Therapy as a healthcare profession?

The idea of music as a healing influence that could affect health and behaviour is as old as the writings of Aristotle and Plato. The 20th century discipline began in the West after World War I and World War II when community musicians of all types, both amateur and professional, went to veterans' hospitals to play for the thousands of veterans suffering both physical and emotional trauma from the wars. The patients' notable physical and emotional responses to music led the doctors and nurses to request the hiring of musicians by the hospitals. It was soon evident that the hospital musicians needed some prior training before entering the facility and so the demand grew for a college curriculum.

The world's first music therapy degree programme was founded at Michigan State University, USA, in 1944. Music therapy did not emerge as an organised profession until 1950 with the establishment of the National Association for Music

Therapy and, thereafter, the formation of the American Association for Music Therapy in 1971. The two associations merged in 1998 to form the American Music Therapy Association (AMTA).

Who is qualified to practise Music Therapy?

This is primarily directed to the organised music curriculum in the western world. We refer here specifically to the United States and more details will be available at the US Information Services in various Indian cities. Details about courses in other western nations are also available at the respective consulates.

Persons who complete one of the approved college music therapy curricula (including an internship) are eligible to sit for the national examination offered by the Certification Board for Music Therapists. Music therapists who successfully complete the independently administered examination hold the music therapist-board certified credential (MT-BC).

Does research support Music Therapy?

The American Music Therapy Association promotes a vast amount of research exploring the benefits of music as therapy through publication of the *Journal of Music Therapy*, *Music Therapy Perspectives* and other sources. A substantial body of literature exists to support the effectiveness of music therapy. Apart from this, there is conclusive evidence that music therapy has existed in a lay form for centuries. Early man used it for every ritual. He instinctively understood its need and used it with fervour, discipline, care and purpose.

What are the misconceptions about Music Therapy?

Since music therapy isn't as yet a mainstream healing activity, it is looked at with a few misconceptions. But it is a fast evolving field and all misconceptions and myths are being blown away in the winds of acceptance and new discovery.

One misconception is that the patient has to have some particular music ability to benefit from music therapy. The fact of the matter is that musical ability or talent is not a prerequisite for benefiting from it. There is another misconception: there is one particular style of music that is more therapeutic than all the rest. This is also not true. All styles of music can be useful in effecting change in a patient's life. The individual's preferences, circumstances and need for treatment, and the patient's goals help determine the types of music a music therapist may use.

Music has a rhythm with a universal appeal and is beyond barriers of culture, creed, nationality and colour.

Can healthy individuals use Music Therapy?

Healthy individuals can use music for stress reduction via active music making, such as drumming, as well as passive listening for relaxation. Music is often a vital support for physical exercise. Music therapy assists labour and delivery and may also be included in this category since pregnancy is regarded as a normal part of women's life cycles.

Music is a part of our lives. It is accessible to every creature created by Nature. One needn't fall ill to use it. A healthy lifestyle constitutes the wholesome use of music on an everyday basis.

Could you elaborate upon the education of a Music Therapist?

The education of a music therapist is unique among college degree programmes because it not only allows a thorough study of music, but also encourages examination of one's self as well as others. The undergraduate curriculum includes coursework in music therapy, psychology, music, biological, social and behavioural sciences, disabilities and general studies.

Entry level study includes practical application of music therapy procedures and techniques learned in the classroom through required fieldwork in facilities serving individuals with disabilities in the community and/or on-campus clinics. Students learn to assess the needs of clients, develop and implement treatment plans, and evaluate and document clinical changes.

At the completion of AMTA-approved academic training and internship, the student is eligible for admission to the certification exam administered by the Certification Board for Music Therapists, Inc. Upon passing the national examination administered by the CBMT, the student acquires the credential Music Therapist-Board Certified (MT-BC). Coursework requirements vary; contact individual American universities for specific information.

What is the future of Music Therapy?

In western countries, particularly the United States, the future of music therapy is promising because state-of-the-art music therapy research in physical rehabilitation, Alzheimer's disease, and psychoneuroimmunology is documenting the effectiveness of music therapy in terms that are important in the context of a biological medical model. It has been proved beyond the pale of doubt that certain music therapy models have conclusive treatment benefits for specific problems.

Music therapy is finally being recognised globally. Newer concepts are emerging by the day, new vistas are beckoning and a whole new breed of therapists and new music therapy curricula are being forged by the minute. The future is exciting and alluring for anybody keen on traversing uncharted waters and making valuable music at the same time.

2. The Miracle of a Brother's Song

This is a touching true account of a young boy's love for his newborn sister. If nothing else, it may bring tears to your eyes and underscore the fact, once gain, of the power of music.

Like any good mother, when Karen found out that another baby was on the way, she did what she could to help her three-year-old son, Michael, prepare for a new sibling. They found out that the new baby was going to be a girl, so day after day and night after night, Michael sang to his sister inside Mummy's tummy. The pregnancy progressed normally for Karen, who lived in Morristown, Tennessee.

Then the labour pains came. Every five minutes... then every minute. But complications arose during delivery. Hours of labour. Would a C-section be required? Finally, little Michael's sister is born.

But she is in a serious condition. A siren howling in the night... the ambulance rushes the infant to the neonatal intensive care unit at St Mary's Hospital.

The days inch by. The little girl gets worse. The paediatric specialist tells the parents, "There is very little hope. Be prepared for the worst."

Karen and her husband contact a local cemetery about a burial plot. They had fixed up a special room in their home, now they plan a funeral.

Michael keeps begging his parents to let him see his sister. "I want to sing to her," he says.

Week number two in Intensive Care. It looks as if a funeral will come before the week is over. Michael keeps nagging about singing to his sister. However, kids are not allowed in Intensive Care.

But Karen makes up her mind. She will take Michael whether they like it or not. If he doesn't see his sister now, he will probably never see her alive.

She dresses him in an oversized scrub suit and marches to get him into ICU. He looks like a walking laundry basket. The head nurse recognises him as a child and bellows, "Get that kid out of here – now! There are NO children allowed in ICU."

The "mother" in Karen rises up strong, and the usually mild-mannered lady glares steel-eyes into the head nurse's face, her lips a firm line, "He is not leaving until he sings to his sister!"

Karen tows Michael to his sister's bedside. He gazes at the tiny infant, losing the battle to live, and he begins to sing. In the pure-hearted voice of a three-year-old, Michael sings: *"You are my sunshine, my only sunshine. You make me happy when skies are grey."*

Instantly, the baby girl responds. Her pulse rate becomes calm and steady.

"Keep on singing, Michael."

"You never know, dear, how much I love you. Please don't take my sunshine away."

The ragged strained breathing becomes as smooth as a kitten's purr.

"Keep on singing, Michael."

Tears conquer the face of the bossy head nurse. Karen glows. Michael sings on.

"You are my sunshine, my only sunshine. Please don't take my sunshine away."

Funeral plans are scrapped. The next day, the very next day, the little girl is well enough to go home!

Woman's Day magazine called it "The Miracle of a Brother's Song".

❑ ❑ ❑

3. A Health Report on the Healing Powers of Music

These reports were presented at the VII International Music Medicine Symposium held in July 1998 at the Faculty of Music, Melbourne University, Australia. All those mentioned participated and provided their input, which we record for the benefit of our readers and a better understanding of music as sheer therapy.

According to Dr Rosalie Rebello-Pratt, Vice President of the International Society for Music in Medicine, and Professor of Music at Brigham Young University in the United States, "What we do is look at these specific effects of music on behaviour. Such as the effects of music on premature infants; physiological parameters; chronic fatigue syndrome in women; anxiety in the dental patient; women in childbirth and so on. Not just any music, we're looking at specific kinds and characteristics of music. Such as the amount of repetition, the amount of melody, tonic chords, things that the ear hears and wants to hear again."

Dr Jane Standley is Professor of Music Therapy at Florida State University in the United States. She's been researching the effect of music on premature babies with feeding difficulties. Her experience makes her believe that music is very effective for babies, particularly those who are in a very stressful environment. "If you can imagine a newborn baby who's going to spend the first two or three months of its life 24 hours a day in an environment with lights and lots of noise and alarm systems and equipment noises from ventilators, and the machines that are keeping the babies alive, you can imagine why good music might be very soothing in that environment," says Dr Standley.

An experiment was conducted wherein commercially recorded lullabies with female vocalists were used for babies to identify with. Newborn babies prefer the female voice because they've heard the mother's voice during the last trimester in the womb. Steady piano or guitar accompaniments were used as opposed to an orchestra where instruments are coming in a flood. This had to be done because each of those factors is an alerting response for the infants, and premature infants, as the ones in the study, are easily overwhelmed.

So a pacifier with an air pressure transducer that converted air pressure to an electrical energy tape recorder was created. Two switches were available; one allows programming the amount of time that the baby receives music, usually about 10 seconds, so if the baby sucks within the 10 seconds, the music will just continue and not get cut off. If the baby fails to suck after 10 seconds, the music cuts off and the baby has to reactivate the music with an additional suck. The other switch allows setting the amount of pressure the baby has to use. So as the baby learns to do this, increasing the pressure that's required increases the baby's endurance. They have to suck a bit harder to keep the music on.

This experiment ran for several months, and the results were that all the babies discriminated when the music was on and off, and increased their sucking rates about 2½ times in order to receive the music reinforcement, and that they very quickly learned the discrimination. It only took about 2½ minutes on an average for the babies to learn the skill.

In an earlier study, using music and massage with agitated premature babies, Dr Standley found that baby boys left hospital 1½ days sooner than those not receiving music. But the females, in typical form, did even better: they left hospital 11 days sooner!

Therapeutic Music for Babies

It's findings like these which have reinforced Dr Fred Schwartz's faith in the value of music for babies. Dr Schwartz is an anaesthetist in the neo-natal ward at Piedmont Hospital in Atlanta, Georgia.

"What we're doing with music is using music to cause a stress reduction for babies," he says, "and this has been replicated in a number of studies. Music can change the behavioural state of an agitated premature baby that perhaps is thrashing the arms, and consuming precious oxygen and calories. So these babies are often blue. When you play music, they stop thrashing, they go into a restful awake or asleep state, and their oxygen saturation actually goes up right before your eyes. The cost of intensive care for premature babies in the United States is about $3.5 billion per year. If we can incorporate music into our neo-natal intensive care units, we can perhaps save 10% or 15% of the total expenditure."

Since the beginning of 1998, every premature baby now receives music as therapy as a matter of course. "We have a system where we have a CD player for every baby. The CD player is mounted on the wall and then the output of that goes into a little computer speaker. The total cost of our music system for every baby is between $400 and $500, and this is a fairly automatic system where all the nurse needs to do is just press the button, No.1 CD; No.2 CD," continues Dr Schwartz.

"We like to start out with something rather simple, perhaps similar to what the babies have been hearing in the womb, so for most premature babies in our intensive care unit, we use womb sound, and female vocal sound music, perhaps for the 20-week to 29-gestational-week premature babies.

"Then they start being able to respond to a little bit more complex music, not over-orchestrated but a lovely lullaby is what these babies respond to very well. And perhaps a classical arrangement that is arranged very, very simply, so that the baby is not overloaded with their senses.

"You can watch the monitors, and within one minute you can see the heart rate going down, the oxygen saturation going up and often a behavioural change fairly immediately. Levels of oxygen in the blood go up and they stay up, and this has long-term consequences as far as helping that baby grow faster," concludes Dr Schwartz.

Dr Tony Wigram, of the University of Aalborg in Denmark, is President of the World Federation of Music Therapy. Talking about babies and music, he points out that lullabies are frequently sung in a soft, gentle voice with gentle timbres: "Whoever heard of a lullaby being played on an oboe, because it's got a more precise and hard timbre. And the music, the melody of a lullaby is quite often a series of short repetitive phrases. So the repetition of the melody and the way the melody may go up a little bit, but then go down, is very significant in its effect."

There has also been some good research on these parameters by an English psychologist John Sloboda, who wrote a very interesting book and several articles on the emotional effects and the language of music. He has researched the musical components that could cause people to have certain reactions like changes in their mood, or feelings of going to sleep, or feelings of sadness. He has also analysed these parameters and the reasons why music can make people feel melancholy, mournful, or sad.

Dr Tony Wigram believes that there are clear parameters in the music, in the falling phrases and the way the melody is structured, and in the repetitive minor rhythm of the harmony. He believes that one can identify the effect of the music by the parameters. And that's why the study of music and the skill of being able to use music is essentially music therapy. "Music therapists need to be skilled musicians, because they need to use those parameters in their interactions with clients," says Dr Wigram.

There is some evidence suggesting that in the baroque era, some compositions were actually written to match the human heartbeat in the belief that music has healing properties to which the body is able to respond. But how the music really does affect the brain was the research interest of Professor Dale Taylor, Director of Music Therapy Studies at the University of Wisconsin-Eau Claire in the United States.

Explaining Music Therapy

"People ask me as a professional music therapist, 'How does music do these things?' and I really couldn't tell them, and that always bothered me," says Professor Taylor. "And so what I've done is to create what I call a biomedical theory of music therapy, and that biomedical theory basically says that music affects human behaviour by affecting the brain. And by knowing what those effects are, they can be replicated. My work shows how music therapy helps decrease stress, lowers anxiety and improves those areas that are damaged when anxiety and stress are at high levels, such as the immune system for example."

Continues Professor Taylor, "The first real attempt that I made at explaining music therapy in terms of brain functioning was to come up with a neurological model for treating aphasia. When those parts of the brain that are damaged are language parts of the brain it is called aphasia. And so what I've done is propose a system for using music to help healthy parts of the brain take over the language functions of the damaged language centres, which in 97% of the population are in the left hemisphere. So what I've done is to use the music functions of the right hemisphere to help regain those functions that were lost through damage to the language centres in the left hemisphere."

According to Professor Taylor, the neurological basis of that recovery process is based on findings showing that when a person talks, the most active parts of the brain are the language centres in the left hemisphere, but when a person is involved in music, the scans of the brain show (by measuring oxygen consumption in different parts of the brain) that much more of the brain, particularly the right hemisphere, is activated. And so there are billions more neurones brought to bear on the task.

"Using music, we can get the brain to start doing some things that it cannot do when there's no music, simply because it's much more of the brain working on it. The brain then will shift that task from the damaged area in the left hemisphere, perhaps over to the right hemisphere in a corresponding area. And because the brain has been shown through lots and lots of research to have that ability to shift functions from one part to another, I call that 'functional plasticity'. And so we're using music to activate the functional plasticity of the human brain," Dr Wigram elaborates.

Dr Wigram believes that the effect on heart rate and blood pressure and other physical parameters has evoked a lot of research, not just from music therapists but from music psychologists as well. And it's a lot to do with arousal levels and with the elements in the music. "What's really important when making this type of research is to define and describe the musical parameters in the music that you're using," he says. "For example, to say somebody's heart rate reduces over a period of 30 minutes when they listen to Mozart, may indicate to the general population that if they go out and get a piece of Mozart and listen to it for 30 minutes their heart rate will go down. But, of course, that can't be true. We have to know which piece of Mozart, and what were the musical parameters in that piece that may have caused heart rate to reduce."

One of Dr Wigram's research areas has been the physiological effect of sound on the body, in particular, low frequency sounds. In some of the research, he found that arousal levels did reduce over time if pulse low frequency sinusoidal vibration together with sedative or relaxing music was used.

"Sedative music is going to be music that's very predictable, because if you have music which has got a lot of surprises in it, where you don't expect sudden crescendos, sudden accents, changes in tempi, then you're always being surprised and your heart rate will fluctuate accordingly," he says. "So if we define the parameters of predictable music as being very stable, very equal level of intensity and without sudden changes in tempo, then I found that over time, heart rates reduce significantly with this type of music. And that can be very useful for somebody who has anxiety or stress-related disorders, who needs to find a way of slowing down."

Emma O'Brien is the music therapist in oncology and palliative care at the Royal Melbourne Hospital. She is a firm believer in the theory that music aids the curative process. "We use music therapy methods to help treat the symptoms for chemotherapy, for bone marrow transplants, and to help patients cope with their treatment and long periods of hospitalisation," she says. "We help alleviate sensory deprivation, feelings of loneliness, emotional stresses and also physical stresses that they may experience as part of the experience of being in hospital and having the diagnosis of cancer."

Communication Disorders

As well as teaching at the University of Aalborg in Denmark, Tony Wigram practises music therapy in Britain. There he works with children with communication and developmental disorders like autism and similar conditions.

"I think the most important area that music therapists are evaluating quite often with children with these particular problems is their social interaction, their imagination and their creativity," says Wigram. "And because of this, you're enabling them, you're empowering them to communicate in a non-verbal way, because most of the conventional ways of communicating for these particular children are quite inhibited, delayed, or disordered. So we're trying to create a potential for them to communicate. But that means that you do need to analyse the musical material: the way they play a drum, the way they bang it, or the instruments they choose to use, and you need to understand by the analysis, what is the meaning of what they're saying. Are they telling you that they're feeling angry, or they're frustrated, or are they telling you that they're happy and they want to communicate with you."

Wigram talks of a five-year-old boy who was referred to him because he was thought to be autistic. He consistently talked about the toilet and mentioned the word 'toilet' about 25 times in the first three minutes of the meeting! He was interested in the toilet because he wanted to watch the water go down, not because he wanted to use the toilet.

"In the music therapy session I didn't use verbal language with him at all," says Wigram. "I gave him some drums to play and he stood with the drum either side, and he banged the sticks up and down. I mean his playing was very skilful; very quickly he showed me that he had great rhythmic capacity. He could hear the rhythms I was playing and reproduce them. And then, what I think was most significant, was that he was able to quickly anticipate and understand turn taking. He played a few notes, then stopped and waited for me. And I played back to him. And we built up a process that was added to by the musical dynamic."

Talking about the child, Wigram says that he became louder, he became softer, he got faster and slower. "Everything was reciprocal and that's quite untypical in children with autism. This little boy showed a great capacity for creative improvisation at the same time in this dialogue as respecting and listening to what I was doing. So it was some very good evidence that this child had much more potential perhaps, at a non-verbal level, for communicating than had previously been estimated because of his rather repetitive and echolalic speech patterns."

Alan Lem, a music therapist and PhD student at the University of Western Sydney, Australia, researches Tibetan bowls. "They are probably the most fascinating sound-producing tools for the purpose of music therapy, because of their multi-frequency characteristics," he says. "A common experience amongst my clients is that the person feels an immediate sensation of warmth and a certain feeling of being centred. People achieve very quickly a state of relaxation when I use the bowls, and also people go very quickly into an altered state of consciousness."

According to Alan, he feels people tend to use conventional music more often than just sound. But he thinks the scope and potential for the use of bowls is tremendous, because "we're dealing with sound more than just music. It means that the client can very often relate quicker, because there are no boundaries, there are no rights and wrongs, as to whether we play a right note or a wrong note".

When the bowls strike, it is a dissonating sound. It is immediately followed by a warm tone. From a psychological point of view, it is pure tension release. It alternates between tension and relaxation. So a person, by listening to these sounds or playing them, can immediately identify with the two states and enter a state of relaxation.

The analysis and the scientific evaluation of the effect of music as therapy is developing, and with the increasing demand in health systems for evidence-based practice, we could easily conclude that there's proportionately a lot more research going on in music therapy than there is in other professions.

❑ ❑ ❑

4. Divine Melodies

That music therapy is catching on in India comes across from the fact that the August 2002 issue of *Life Positive* – India's first body-mind-spirit magazine – has devoted two articles to this topic.

The first article by Arundhati Bhanot, titled *The Sound of World Music*, delves on the large number of international artists who have been drawn towards India, thanks to its rich history of melody. These foreign musicians collaborated with Indian musicians to create a fusion of soulful melodies meant to relax the body, mind and spirit.

It all began in the early 1970s when Osho (then Bhagwan Rajneesh) opened his ashram in Pune. Amongst his numerous acolytes were renowned musicians like Deuter, whose musical accompaniment to Osho's series on meditation became famous. Deuter mixes acoustic and electronic instruments, ethnic influences and sounds from nature, which is just the right mix for those looking to meditate or relax. Deuter's music is used extensively by medical and psychological practitioners in therapy.

Then followed musicians like John 'Mahavishnu' McLaughlin, a disciple of the US-based guru Sri Chinmoy, who created a style that was ethereal as well as universal, inspiring a series of richly spiritual fusion albums. Another notable name in world music is James Asher, who utilises hypnotic and enchanting rhythms from tribal and folk music.

In an article titled *Rhythm Divine That Heals*, Nishtha Shukla writes about Delhi-based consultant physician cardiologist Dr Neelam Verma's success with her holistic Cosmic Healing Centre.

"Music therapy is a symphony of colour, time, music, the heart and the chakras within – living on a higher plane which uplifts the mood and emotions," says Dr Neelam Verma. In August 2002, Dr Verma launched her collection of five cassettes titled *Healing Rhythms of Devotion*, under the Cosmic Rhythms label. The five cassettes are titled *Haridhun Samkeertan, Rhythm of Peace, Divine Dawn, Harmonised Pranayam* and *Healing Touch*.

The cardiologist believes that "appropriate music can help in one's healing process and is like a flow of healing energy within". Dr Neelam believes that for people who are tired and stressed out, the right music and shlokas can help: "They work on a subtle energy plane to insulate you from your surroundings."

She firmly believes that sound plays an important role in people's lives and has a tremendous impact on the psyche. In this connection, she says our Scriptures teach a lot about the positive influence of music and dance on healing. "It is well-established that a certain kind of music, played at a particular time of the day, can be relaxing," she opines. Apart from musical notes, the expression and intonation of words is also important.

However, Dr Neelam stresses that she uses music not as an alternative to medical treatment, but as a complementary therapy. The music she has compiled using improvised ragas is meant to work as a support system to help a person recuperate from immense stress and tension. It can be used for terminal patients, aftercare, for rehabilitating children with disabilities as well as those in semi-coma. Not to mention the average person who may be seemingly healthy but ends up feeling down in the dumps.

With mainstream practitioners slowly recognising the value of music in therapy, the position of music therapy should gradually see an upswing in India in the years to come.

❑ ❑ ❑

Bibliography

1. Bruscia, K.E., *Defining Music Therapy*, (Spring House Books, 1989).

2. Beaulieu, John, *Music and Sound in the Healing Arts*, (New York: Tallman, 1987).

3. Campbell, Don, *The Mozart Effect: Tapping the Power of Music to Heal the Body, Strengthen the Mind, and Unlock the Creative Spirit*, (New York: Avon Books, 1997).

4. Chopra, Deepak, MD, *Quantum Healing: Exploring the Frontiers of Mind/Body Medicine*, (Bantam Books, New York, 1989).

5. Goleman, D., & Gruin, J., *Mind Body Medicine*, (New York: Consumer Reports Books, 1993).

6. Keyes, Laurel E., *Toning: The Creative Power of the Voice*, (Marina delRey, California: Devorss and Co., 1973).

7. Krippner, S., *The Highest State of Consciousness*, (New York: Doubleday & Co., 1972).

8. Le Mee, Katherine, *Chant: The Origins, Form, Practice, and Healing Power of Gregorian Chant*, (New York: Bell Tower, 1994).

WATER
A Miracle Therapy
—A.R. Hari

The more science has advanced, the further away have we moved from Mother Nature. Thanks to our artificial existence, even to quench a natural urge like thirst, we imbibe synthetic substances such as colas and caffeine-loaded drinks.

Having starved our body of Nature's most precious liquid, water, we are beset with multiple ailments like headaches, arthritis, asthma, urinary problems, general debility, blood pressure and the like. Missing the root cause of the problem, we rush to doctors—only to have antibiotics pumped into us that offer short-term "relief" while turning into long-term nightmares.

This book shows how drinking just 12 to 14 glasses of water per day (for the average person) cures many ailments, including chronic ones. Incredibly, by just carefully following the 'Water Protocol' in the book, you may feel the difference within 48 hours! Just like a water-starved house plant that springs to attention within minutes of being watered.

Demy Size • Pages: 112
Price: Rs. 80/- • Postage: Rs. 15/-

The Magic of
Aromatherapy
—Gwydion O'Hara

Breathe in the intoxicating aroma of lavender, orange and pine to relieve stress. Attract unconditional love by sprinkling rose, jasmine, carnation and apple into a steaming bath. From therapeutic applications for massage, pain relief, and mental clarity to magical applications for love, prosperity, and ritual, the 332 recipes in *The Magic of Aromatherapy* will help you balance your physical, mental, and spiritual selves.

But you'll get more than just recipes in this unusually complete guide. You'll learn the 'why' of essential oils—traditional, historical and cultural uses—plus you get an exhaustive reference section with planetary, astrological, elemental and gender associations; magical and therapeutic properties; magical cross-references; and a listing of oil sources.

Demy Size • Pages: 264
Price: Rs. 108/- • Postage: Rs. 15/-

Fruit and Vegetable Juice Therapy

—Dr. Syed Aziz Ahmad & Dr. S.C. Sharma

Did you know that papaya, orange, lemon and pomegranate act as antidotes to high blood pressure... or *amla* and carrot are useful in controlling asthma... or guava and *mosambi* help in regulating constipation? In fact, each and every fruit and vegetable has incredible curative properties, and offers a natural way to good health. Fruits and vegetables act as scavengers to our body, and drive away toxic and harmful wastes. They nourish our body with pure water, sugar, vitamins, minerals, proteins, fibres, aromatic compounds and a host of other micro-nutrients. Grab this authentic, self-help, therapeutic guide to learn and apply the remarkable ways to combat naturally all kinds of ailments. Some examples—

❖ High B.P. antidotes: Papaya, orange, lemon, pomegranate.
❖ Skin disease preventives: Apple, carrot, watermelon, lemon.
❖ Diarrhoea curatives: Pineapple, apple, pomegranate.
❖ Constipation regulators: Guava, *mosambi*, apple.
❖ Digestion aid: Spinach (*palak*).
❖ Diabetic control: Bitter gourd (*karela*).
❖ Jaundice & Diarrhoea control: Carrot.

Demy Size • Pages: 224
Price: Rs. 96/- • Postage: Rs. 15/-

The Practical Book of REIKI

—Mrs. Rashmi Sharma &
Maharaj Krishan Sharma

Healing Through
Universal Lifeforce Energy

Find balance and harmony in the mind and spirit. It is truly a gift to yourself! Increase your vibratory level and healing capacity by treating yourself and others. Be sure to engage your intuitive knowledge, feel free so that you can maintain the accelerated ability to channel the Reiki energy. Remove the energy blocks and negative thoughts from Chakras and personality traits.

Apply Reiki by following the five principles:
❖ Just for today I will live with attitude of gratitude
❖ Just for today I will not worry
❖ Just for today I will not be angry
❖ Just for today I will do my work honestly
❖ Just for today I will show love and respect for every living thing.

This unique book is for those who are looking for a useful treatise for self-treatment and transformation with the principles of Reiki.

Big Size • Pages: 168
Price: Rs. 96/- • Postage: Rs. 15/-

The Healing Power of Mudras

The Yoga of the Hands

—Rajendar Menen

Our fingers have enormous power.

With the right positioning for prescribed periods, the fingers of both hands can rejuvenate the body, heal disease and even slowly, over time, lead to a spiritual awakening.

Mudras can be practised in almost any posture: walking, sitting, standing and even lying down! They require no gadgetry, complicated accessories or extra space. They are easy to do, make no demands of extraordinary physical strength, and are completely free.

Called the 'Yoga of the hands', Mudras are an ideal healing tool. They have been known to prevent and cure illnesses and, most important, slowly bring about a spiritual regeneration.

The Healing Power of Mudras details several beneficial Mudras, and provides a holistic view of physical and spiritual healing.

The right colours, foods, thoughts and ambience combined with regular Mudra practice will make for a new and healthy you!

Demy Size • Pages: 104
Price: Rs. 80/- • Postage: Rs. 15/-

Master Approaches to New Age Alternative Therapies

—Luis S.R. Vas

Physical health is closely linked to mental and spiritual health. In fact, very often a physical ailment is but a manifestation of a problem at the psychological level. As such, people down the ages have tried to explore this inextricable connection and come out with incredible solutions to a variety of ailments.

This book is a masterly volume providing an overview of the different approaches propounded by thinkers and researchers over time. For instance, Choa Kok Sui, a Filipino practising Pranic Healing claiming to cure illnesses of eye, liver, kidney, heart in a few sessions through it. Dr. Benedict Lust believed that man could stay healthy and strong as long as he lived in accordance with Natural laws and Yogic practices, as given in an organised system by Maharshi Patanjali in the first century B.C. and known to be a miracle cure for a range of illnesses. Including these, the book brings the basic theories and practices of over 30 such masters from every part of the globe—ranging from Rosemary Gladstar, John Robbin, and Lama Surya Das to Indian masters and Ancient masters.

Demy Size • Pages: 200
Price: Rs. 80/- • Postage: Rs. 15/-

Magneto-Therapy
The miraculous healing power
—*Rajendar Menen*

Be it an ailment that has you at your wits' end or the fact that you simply seek to enhance your general well-being without burning a hole in your pocket or suffering unforeseen side effects, magneto-therapy is just the right choice for you.

The book is divided into two sections. Section I focuses on magnets, magnetism and magneto-therapy in general and its status in India, while Section II deals with the scenario in the West regarding research, treatments and advances in magneto-therapy. From the origins of magneto-therapy to its current status, from everyday cures to the larger influence of magnets on our lives, from products that are easily available to experiments conducted with magnets all over the world on human, plant and animal life, you will find all this and much more in the book.

If practised properly and diligently, before long, you should be eating well, sleeping well and feeling a general sense of well-being at all times.

Demy Size • Pages: 128
Price: Rs. 80/- • Postage: Rs. 15/-

Colour Therapy
The Miracle of Sun Rays
—*Mrs. Rashmi Sharma & Maharaj Krishan Sharma*

The author of this book, Ms. Rashmi Sharma, is a specialist in Herbal Beauty Treatments, Naturopathy and Reiki. She also leads Herbal Educational Society in Delhi.

The author, in collaboration with her experienced colleagues, has tried to compile her findings in a very simple and understandable way so that even common readers could find it interesting and beneficial.

❖ Know how to cure specific ailments by adjusting the colour input to the body ❖ Understand how body gives out an unbalanced pattern of vibration ❖ Know how Colour Therapy works to restore the balance of the body ❖ Treat and cure any disorder of the body—be it mental, emotional, metabolic or physical.

The book will be useful if the readers act on the methods as recorded, practically for their own health and others—at a very low cost. The ways explained in the book are so simple that even a layman can follow, and derive maximum benefits from it. Everything you need to know to get well and stay well—and here is the book you are searching for!

Demy Size • Pages: 80
Price: Rs. 60/- • Postage: Rs. 20/-